Contract Planning and Contractual Procedures

Quarter

Macmillan Building and Surveying Series

Series Editor: IVOR H. SEELEY
Emeritus Professor, The Nottingham Trent University

Contract Planning and Contractual Procedures

B. Cooke

M.Sc., C. Eng., M.I.C.E., M.C.I.O.B., F.R.I.C.S.
Principal Lecturer in Building,
Liverpool John Moore's University

Third Edition

MACMILLAN

First published 1981 by
THE MACMILLAN PRESS LTD
Houndmills, Basingstoke, Hampshire RG21 2XS
and London
Companies and representatives
throughout the world

ISBN 0–333–57760–4

A catalogue record for this book is available
from the British Library.

Printed in China

First edition 1981
Reprinted (with corrections) 1983
Second edition 1984
Reprinted 1986
Third edition 1992
Reprinted 1993 (twice)

Series Standing Order
If you would like to receive future titles in this series as they are published, you can
make use of our standing order facility. To place a standing order please contact your
bookseller or, in case of difficulty,write to us at the address below with your name
and address and the name of the series. Please state with which title you wish to
begin your standing order. (If you live outside the United Kingdom we may not have
the rights for your area, in which case we will forward your order to the publisher
concerned.)

Customer Services Department, Macmillan Distribution Ltd
Houndmills, Basingstoke, Hampshire RG21 2XS, England

CONTENTS

LIST OF EXAMPLES

ACKNOWLEDGEMENTS

The author wishes to acknowledge the encouragement received from Professor I.H. Seeley for his guidance and advice during the editing. I am also indebted to Professor W.B. Jepson for his initial enthusiasm in encouraging me to write the book together with his advice on its content. The author is indebted to Alice Roberts for so ably typing the manuscript together with Malcolm Stewart for assistance during publication. My special thanks are due to my management students at Stockport College of Technology for their participation in the many worked examples during college lectures.

PREFACE

The aim of the book is to provide a systematic appraisal of the
planning procedures and management decisions undertaken during
the pre-tender stage, pre-contract and contract planning stage.
This includes considerations relating to the decision to tender
and the tender adjudication. Procedures outlined follow the
recommendations of the Code of Estimating Practice as set out by
the Chartered Institute of Building.

Examples of the various stages of tender preparation are outlined from procedures utilised by both medium and large-sized
contracting organisations. The format of the pre-tender meeting,
site visit report and examples of method statements are illustrated.
Sources of estimating information are outlined together with
procedures for obtaining quotations. A check list for contract
preliminaries is indicated and the points to be considered at
tender adjudication outlined. The controversial matter of bidding
strategy is outlined in principle and a method of analysing tender
performance presented.

The planning considerations prior to convening a contract are
outlined and a number of examples are presented on site layout
planning. Examples are shown of various requirement schedules
which form an important part of the planning process and assist
in calling information forward from both the architect and other
consultants. Budgetary control forms an essential part of the
pre-contract planning procedures. Examples of various types of
budgets are discussed together with a cash flow assessment for a
contract and considerations for improving the cash flow situation.

The various types of planning techniques available to the
contractor are illustrated together with examples of sequence
studies for individual trade gangs. Network and precedence
diagrams are outlined in principle together with examples showing
the application of lead and lag terminology and crash costing
techniques. The application of monthly planning and weekly
planning techniques are shown together with their relationship to
site meetings. The importance of progress recording and the
preparation of accurate weekly reports as an aid to control are
discussed. An example is presented of a weekly pre-target based
cost system together with the basic principles of a planning
orientated materials control system.

The reference will provide prospective site management personnel
with an insight to all stages in the planning cycle. The requirements of the Chartered Institute of Building – Final Part II
building production paper syllabus are covered together with

Contract management papers in the Institute of Quantity Surveyors examinations.   Undergraduates on building degree courses will also find the reference useful as an insight into contractual procedures.

The third edition of this book has been updated to include changes in the approach to the assessment of contract preliminaries - consideration for time and fixed related costs in relation to site requirements, plant and employers' requirements. A new chapter has been added in relation to the planning and feasibility requirements of speculative building projects.

B. COOKE

Stockport,
Spring 1992

1   THE PLANNING PROCESS

Planning procedures in the construction industry appear to vary
widely between companies.   They tend to be governed by the following factors

(1) The size and management structure of the business organisation.
The size of the firm may be determined for statistical purposes by
reference to its annual turnover or to the number of employees.
It is only a guide and a convenience as the two may not correspond
and a firm with a large turnover may have very little direct labour.
Other factors include the magnitude and location of the work itself,
its complexity in both technical and managerial terms, and the level
of capability to which the firm aspires;   these all influence organisation and control.

    The construction team for a complex building project may repre-
sent a large manufacturing and marketing concern while on the other
hand a labour intensive activity may call on little by way of plant
and finance to support it.

    In terms of planning and control the plan establishes production
objectives, while control systems are designed to review performance in relation to them, and to report deviations which might call
for action.   Any communication gap between site activity and responsibility may call for action.   A site which is visited frequently by the proprietor of the firm may result in planning and
control being undertaken mainly verbally and informally, action
being in response to a visit.   Where decisions on finance, plant
and staffing have to be made for distant sites a more detailed and
complex control system is needed.   In the latter case the objectives of the firm and its plans must be stated formally and in more
detail.

    Planning policy is thus a response to the firm's perception of
its control needs and the objective standards it sets in order to
achieve them.

(2) The type, nature and varying range of work undertaken.
Many organisations limit the type of work undertaken or specialise
in certain types of construction, e.g. a medium-sized company may
specialise in housing work on a speculative or contract basis
while others limit their work range to industrial projects.

(3) The planning policy within the organisation.   This stems
from the policy laid down by the principal or board of directors.
This may arise from the awareness of senior managers towards
planning objectives and may be related to the background or experience of individual members of the management team.

1

(4) The technical and managerial expertise represented by the company.

1.1 THE PLANNING STAGES INVOLVED IN THE CONSTRUCTION PROCESS

Stage 1: Pre-tender Planning

This is the planning carried out during the preparation of an estimate as a contribution to a tender or bid.

   Recommended procedures of pre-tender planning are set out in the Institute of Building Code of Estimating Practice.[1]

   The time period for carrying out pre-tender planning activities may vary from one week to three months, depending upon the nature of the enquiry.

   The RIBA Code of Practice[2] recommends that a minimum period of four weeks should be allowed for the preparation of a realistic bid.

Stage 2: Pre-contract Planning

This is the planning which takes place after the award of a contract, immediately prior to the commencement of construction work on the project.

   Again the time period for pre-contract planning activities varies widely. The date of possession of the site is normally stated in the contract documents. Time periods of up to six weeks are, however, common practice.

   It is frequently a requirement of the contract that the client and architect should be furnished with a programme. This may be a presentation based on the contractor's own detailed programme. The purpose of this requirement is that the client should have some guide as to the intentions of the contractor. On the other hand, the contractor frequently enters key dates for the provision of information. The document later becomes reference material whenever claims arise from delays.

Stage 3: Contract Planning

This is the planning which takes place during the building process. It is the responsibility of the contractor to complete the contract within the specified time period. Contract planning activities establish standards against which progress can be reviewed at regular intervals during construction. To complete the project within the contract period demands action to correct for any short-falls in such progress and contract planning is thus part of control Control entails additional expense and thus the resources to be applied in its pursuit are judged in relation to the business risks involved. Figure 1.1 indicates the planning process encompassing the three stages involved.

THE PLANNING PROCESS

PRE-TENDER PLANNING

- DECISION TO TENDER
- PRE-TENDER REPORT
- SITE VISIT REPORT
- ENQUIRIES TO SUBCONTRACTORS AND SUPPLIERS
- STATEMENT OF METHODS
- ESTIMATE BUILD-UP
- PRE-TENDER PROGRAMME
- PRELIMINARIES BUILD-UP
- ESTIMATE ADJUDICATION
- ANALYSIS OF RESULTS

PRE-CONTRACT PLANNING

- PRE-CONTRACT MEETING
- PRE-CONTRACT CHECK LIST
- SUBCONTRACT ORDERS
- SITE LAYOUT PLANNING
- REQUIREMENT SCHEDULES
- MASTER PROGRAMME
- COMMENCEMENT ARRANGEMENTS
- PREPARATION OF CONTRACT BUDGETS

CONTRACT PLANNING

- MONTHLY AND SIX-WEEKLY PLANNING
- WEEKLY PLANNING
- DAILY PLANNING
- PROGRESS REPORTING
- UPDATING OF PROGRESS

Figure 1.1

-TENDER PLANNING STAGE

aration of an estimate and its ultimate adjudication to
formulate a tender follows a similar process in most organisations.

The procedures used within a smaller organisation may, however,
be less formal than in the more complex and larger one.

Larger organisations adopt a more formal approach to estimating
as the responsibility is shared among a construction, estimating
and buying team, with senior management adjudicating, e.g. deciding
how to convert the estimated net cost into the price they wish to
bid.

The stages involved during the preparation of an estimate are
as follows

(1)   The decision to tender
(2)   The pre-tender report
(3)   The site visit report
(4)   Enquiries to subcontractors and suppliers
(5)   The statement of construction methods
(6)   The build-up of the estimate rates
(7)   The pre-tender programme
(8)   The preliminaries build-up
(9)   The estimate adjudication
(10) Analysis of results

The above sequence of events takes place during the estimating
process within the structure of the medium to large firm.   The
Institute of Building, within the Code of Estimating Practice,[1]
illustrates various estimating forms which may be of assistance
in standardising estimating procedures.

1.3   PRE-CONTRACT PLANNING STAGE

A contract is a commitment.   When the contractor has accepted this,
he must review the information available to him and establish his
plan.   Decisions must be made relating to the financing of the
contract, the appointment of subcontractors and suppliers and the
availability of information requirements and resources.   Budgets,
plans of action and programmes must be prepared.   A cash flow
assessment will indicate the funds which may be required to finance
the contract, and the necessary loans can be raised.

The stages involved during pre-contract planning are

(1)   The pre-contract report and meeting
(2)   Pre-contract check list
(3)   Placing of subcontracts - suppliers and subcontractors
(4)   Site layout planning

4

(5) Schedules of requirements
(6) Preparation of master programme
(7) Arrangements for commencing work
(8) Preparation of contract budgets

Standard proformas can again be used for the various stages involved. The prospective site manager should become involved in the planning activities as these are, in effect, an attempt to formulate the method he will adopt. In particular the drawings and bills of quantities must be reviewed in order to assess essential requirements for the early stages of the contract, so that the immediate resources can be earmarked.

Budgets will be prepared in order to forecast cumulative value and cost. A cash flow assessment may be developed from budgetary control procedures and a valuation forecast prepared. Preliminaries and plant budgets can be prepared against which actual costs may be matched during the contract.

Without a plan against which to monitor performance, there can be no control. The terms in which the plan is stated are conditioned by the form of control which the firm proposes to exercise.

1.4 CONTRACT PLANNING

The stages involved in contract planning during a project may be summarised as follows

(1) Six-weekly and monthly planning review
(2) Weekly or short term planning
(3) Daily planning
(4) Monthly and weekly reports of progress
(5) Updating of progress and comparison of budget with performance

The contract planning stages of a contract enable requirements and progress to be reviewed monthly and weekly. Site meetings at monthly intervals with the architect, consultant and subcontractors form an integral part of the planning process. Weekly meetings at site foreman level aim at keeping the monthly programme under review by detailed planning of labour and plant resources for the next five-day period.

Figure 1.2 indicates the relationship between programmes prepared at the pre-tender, pre-contract and contract planning stages.

5

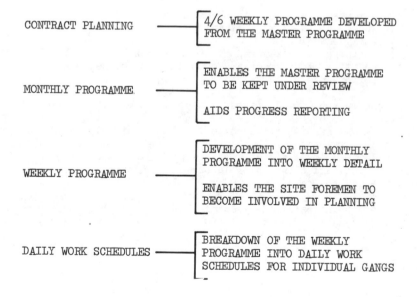

PRE-TENDER PROGRAMME —
- FORMS THE BASIS OF THE TENDER FOR THE BUILD-UP OF CONTRACT PRELIMINARIES
- PRESENTED IN BAR CHART FORMAT IN RELATION TO MAJOR OPERATIONS

PRE-CONTRACT OR MASTER PROGRAMME —
- DEVELOPMENT OF PRE-TENDER PROGRAMME
- PRESENTED IN BAR CHART FORMAT/ NETWORK OR LINE OF BALANCE
- SUBCONTRACTORS, NOMINATIONS AND REQUIREMENT DATES

CONTRACT PLANNING —
- 4/6 WEEKLY PROGRAMME DEVELOPED FROM THE MASTER PROGRAMME

MONTHLY PROGRAMME —
- ENABLES THE MASTER PROGRAMME TO BE KEPT UNDER REVIEW
- AIDS PROGRESS REPORTING

WEEKLY PROGRAMME —
- DEVELOPMENT OF THE MONTHLY PROGRAMME INTO WEEKLY DETAIL
- ENABLES THE SITE FOREMEN TO BECOME INVOLVED IN PLANNING

DAILY WORK SCHEDULES —
- BREAKDOWN OF THE WEEKLY PROGRAMME INTO DAILY WORK SCHEDULES FOR INDIVIDUAL GANGS

Figure 1.2

6

REFERENCES - THE PLANNING PROCESS

1. The Institute of Building Code of Estimating Practice
    Fourth Edition, 1979

2. National Joint Consultative Committee - Code of Procedure
    for Single Stage Selective Tendering, R.I.B.A. 1977

BIBLIOGRAPHY

Pilcher, R., Principles of Construction Management,
    2nd Edition (McGraw-Hill, 1979)

Calvert, R.E., Introduction to Building Management,
    3rd Edition (Newnes Butterworth, 1979)

Oxley, R. and Poskit, J., Management Techniques Applied to the
    Construction Industry, 3rd Edition (Crosby Lockwood, 1980)

Harper, D.R., The Process and the Product (The Construction
    Press, 1978)

2 PRE-TENDER PLANNING

The following selective topic areas on pre-tender planning follow the order of the tendering process within medium to large contracting firms.

Main points relating to the principal factors to be considered at each stage are included. Various tendering proformas used by construction organisations are included in a simplified format together with reference to both the Institute of Building Code of Estimating practice[1] and published research papers in the bibliography.

Topic areas included are as follows

2.1 Tendering policy - the decision to tender

2.2 Initial pre-tender meeting

2.3 Site visit report information

2.4 Objectives of method statements

2.5 Examples on the preparation of method statements

2.6 Sources of estimating information

2.7 Obtaining quotations from subcontractors and suppliers

2.8 Build-up of the estimate

2.9 Build-up of contract preliminaries

2.10 Adjudication of an estimate

2.11 Analysis of performance and bidding theory

2.12 Analysis of tender performance - worked example

2.1 TENDERING POLICY - THE DECISION TO TENDER

A medium-sized contracting organisation, engaged in speculative housing and industrial development projects, is considering expanding into public and commercial contracting.

The following factors will influence tendering policy in general and further factors, which should be considered in the light of prospective changes of policy, are outlined.

2.1.1 General Tendering Policy Factors

(1) Current workload - commitment on contracts in progress

(2) Workload in the estimating and surveying departments

(3) Capital available to finance new projects - effect on capital commitment on current projects

(4) Availability of resources in terms of both staff and labour

(5) Availability of plant resources

(6) Type and location of job. Any departure in either characteristic from current trading should be reviewed

(7) Size, nature and value of project. Again departure from current trading patterns must be reviewed

(8) Extent or value of own work in relation to that of nominated subcontractors and suppliers

(9) Degree of competition - number of competitors

(10) Previous knowledge of architect, client, quantity surveyor and consultants

(11) Previous knowledge of nominated subcontractors and suppliers

(12) Terms and conditions of contract. These will include an appraisal of

    (a) The contract period
    (b) Extent of liquidated damages
    (c) Retention limits
    (d) Defects liability period
    (e) Extent or provision of bond
    (f) Fixed price or fluctuating contract

(13) The availability and characteristics of labour in the vicinity of the contract. Alternative opportunities, degree of trade union influence and pay policy of competitors

(14) Time available to prepare tender

(15) Market conditions at the time of the tender submission. The market conditions likely to affect tendering are

    (a) General market conditions in relation to the availability of contract work; number of enquiries received

    (b) Availability of finance; current interest rates/ bank rate.

    (c) Government policy and its effect on the construction industry. Funds allocated to school building, road construction and industrial development areas may encourage or depress activity. The availability of grants for areas of redevelopment and grants available to industry are other important factors.

9

The contractor is well experienced in housing and industrial contracts. He would be well advised to maintain competitive tendering for work of a similar type. To consider expanding into contract work of a different nature introduces new risks and demands a different mix of resources. The contractor must firstly assess an appropriate rate of return on capital invested in the new contracting venture. If it cannot be achieved by careful selection of tenders and the provision of an adequate mark up at adjudication stage, then to submit a tender might involve losses until the firm is able to adjust to changed circumstances.

In the case in question the proposal is to move from sectors (housing and industrial buildings) where by stage payments or short contract durations the firm can expect to gain reimbursement and revenue relatively rapidly, to a sector where payment may be less readily obtained. In the public sector and in contracts of relatively long duration the process of negotiating payment can be more complex.

Both housing and industrial building involve considerable repetition, little work at great heights, few high quality finishings, and relatively simple service installations. The firm should review the experience of existing staff, its resources of plant (it may have no tower cranes or passenger lifts for instance), and the resources of information which it must exploit to gain work.

A paper published by the Institute of Building, Estimating Service Paper No.33 'The Administration of a Tender',[2] indicates the use of an estimating register and an estimating workload chart. Further points relating to the decision to tender are indicated in Section 3 of the Code of Estimating Practice.[1]

A supplement to the Institute of Building Code of Estimating Practice, 'Information required before Estimating',[3] outlines information to be considered before a decision is made to tender.

The information which should be offered along with an invitation to tender and other factors which should be taken into account by management is included as a check list of items as follows

(a) Information required to enable a decision to be made whether or not to tender

  (1) Location of site
  (2) Name of client, architect and quantity surveyor
  (3) Other consultants
  (4) Description of project
  (5) Requirements: commencement and completion dates
  (6) Principal trades to be nominated
  (7) Proposed contractual basis
  (8) Details of documents and information provided
  (9) Key dates for return of tender
  (10) Tender particulars
  (11) Latest date for receipt of acceptance of invitation
  (12) Number of tenders invited

(b) Additional information which should be taken into account by management

    (1) Financial resources
    (2) Market conditions
    (3) Construction problems
    (4) Previous experience of similar types of project
    (5) Previous experience with consultants
    (6) Adequacy of tender information
    (7) Resources necessary to carry out project
    (8) Construction workload
    (9) Estimating workload
  (10) Seasonal risks
  (11) Risks imposed by conditions of contract
  (12) Time available in which to tender

2.2 INITIAL PRE-TENDER MEETING

The detailed procedures for an initial pre-tender planning meeting held within a large contracting organisation are outlined. The responsibilities of the personnel involved during the preparation of the estimate are also to be indicated.

2.2.1 Initial Tender Meeting Procedure

The purpose of the initial tender meeting is to plan and phase the activities of the tender. The meeting, of which minutes should be taken, will be held as soon as possible after the decision to tender has been taken.

2.2.2 Personnel to Attend the Pre-tender Planning Meeting

    General Manager/Director - to act as Meeting Chairman
    Chief Estimator
    Contracts Manager
    Planning Engineer
    Buyer
    Office Manager
    Job Estimator

2.2.3 Main Items to be Considered at the Meeting

(1) The meeting chairman will determine the project category. The enquiry may be graded according to the degree of interest shown by the company, for instance

Category A. Full treatment - Anxious to obtain, submit a keen competitive bid, likely to be adjudicated keenly.

Category B. Detailed treatment - Prepared to invest reasonable estimating effort to gain work. Adjudication likely to be only on modest terms of risk.

Category C. Routine treat- - Adjudication likely to be such that
            ment only   contract will only be won at a good
                             margin.

Category D. Minimal   - Policy submission only with no real
            treatment   likelihood of winning.

A significant planning contribution is only likely to be sought
in categories A and B work.   In category A, alternative schemes
may be reviewed and special plant and equipment considered.   In
category B, the work is likely to be based on existing resources
of equipment, skill and knowledge.

Categories C and D tenders may require little more than a review of the proposed contract period and comments on any critical
activities.

The particulars of the contract will be outlined and the Enquiry
Record proforma (Form 1, I.O.B. Code of Estimating Practice[1]) would
be used to summarise the contract particulars.

(2) A programme of pre-tender activities, or a pre-tender
check list, will be drafted indicating the key dates when information must be available to the job estimator.

The pre-tender check list of the format indicated in Figure 2.1
may be used.   Alternatively, the tender activities may be indicated in bar chart format as illustrated in Figure 2.2.   A programme of pre-tender stages will prove especially advantageous
where the co-ordination of information and dates is essential, as
when consultants are engaged to assist with tender preparation.

(3) A meeting will be held when data relating to the estimate
has been brought together for consideration.

2.2.4 Responsibilities of the Personnel Involved in the Tender
       Preparation

(1) General Manager/Director

  (i) to act as chairman at the initial and main tender meeting
       and brief personnel on their duties during the estimate
       preparation

 (ii) to ensure that scheduled dates as set out in the pre-tender
       check list are seen to be achievable and are recognised by
       those concerned

(iii) to be alive to general market conditions and current events
       which may influence the tender

 (iv) to adjudicate the estimate on its completion, assisted by
       senior management.

12

PRE-TENDER CHECK LIST			
CONTRACT DATE DOCUMENTS RECEIVED	DATE DATE TENDER RETURNED		
REF. PRE-TENDER ACTIVITY	LATEST DATE INFORM- ATION REQUIRED	ACTUAL DATE INFORM- ATION RECEIVED	PERSON RESPON- SIBLE
1 DECISION TO TENDER			
2 ARCHITECT/ENGINEER VISITED			
3 MATERIAL SCHEDULES PREPARED			
4 ENQUIRIES SENT OUT			
5 SITE VISIT REPORT			
6 STATEMENT OF CONSTRUCTION METHOD			
7 ESTIMATE STAGE 1 BUILD-UP			
8 FINAL QUOTATIONS RECEIVED			
9 ESTIMATE STAGE 2 BUILD-UP			
10 PRE-TENDER PROGRAMME			
11 PRELIMINARIES ASSESSMENT			
12 ESTIMATE COMPLETE			
13 ESTIMATE CHECKED			
14 FINAL SUMMARIES			
15 TENDER ADJUDICATION			
16 PRICE MARK UP AGREED			
17 TENDER SUBMITTED			
TENDER NO.	PREPARED BY:		

Figure 2.1

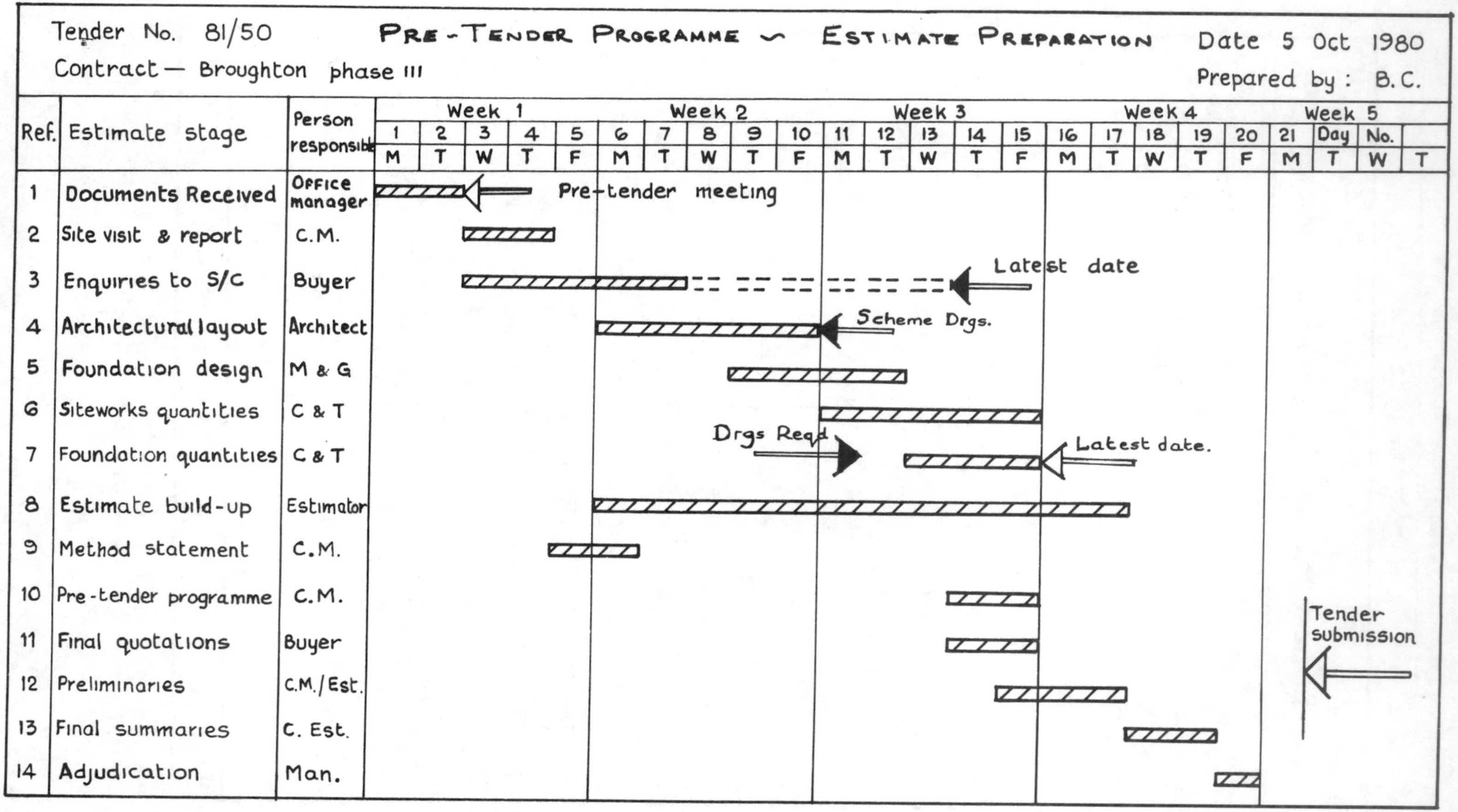

Tender No. 81/50   **PRE-TENDER PROGRAMME ~ ESTIMATE PREPARATION**   Date 5 Oct 1980

Contract— Broughton phase III   Prepared by: B.C.

Ref.	Estimate stage	Person responsible	Week 1					Week 2					Week 3					Week 4					Week 5			
			M	T	W	T	F	M	T	W	T	F	M	T	W	T	F	M	T	W	T	F	M	T	W	T
		Day No.	1	2	3	4	5	6	7	8	9	10	11	12	13	14	15	16	17	18	19	20	21			
1	Documents Received	Office manager																									
2	Site visit & report	C.M.																									
3	Enquiries to S/C	Buyer																									
4	Architectural layout	Architect																									
5	Foundation design	M & G																									
6	Siteworks quantities	C & T																									
7	Foundation quantities	C & T																									
8	Estimate build-up	Estimator																									
9	Method statement	C.M.																									
10	Pre-tender programme	C.M.																									
11	Final quotations	Buyer																									
12	Preliminaries	C.M./Est.																									
13	Final summaries	C. Est.																									
14	Adjudication	Man.																									

Pre-tender meeting

Latest date

Scheme Drgs.

Drgs Reqd

Latest date.

Tender submission

Figure 2.2

(2) Chief Estimator

To control and monitor the collection of tender information and
feed the data to the job estimator. To guide and check the
estimator's work throughout the tender preparation. To assist
in adjudication and to ensure that all consequent adjustments are
checked.

(3) Contracts Manager

To assist the job estimator in the preparation of the site visit
report. To prepare the statement of construction methods indicating the plant requirements to be included in the preliminaries.
The contracts manager will also give advice to the planning engineer
regarding the preparation of the pre-tender programme.

Within certain organisations the contracts manager may be required to give advice on the staffing requirements for inclusion
in the contract preliminaries.

This is not the ideal arrangement unless the contracts manager
is accountable to his firm for the method used and the supervisor
on site is to be under his direction. If a site manager is to
be appointed who will be held accountable for performance, then
sequence and method are his responsibility and the plan should
reflect them. Some firms have rotated site managers through
estimating, production and surveying sections so that they super-
vised and accounted for work for which they successfully estimated.
Responsibility may therefore reflect the inflexibility and organisational uncertainty of the large and complex organisation which
depends on visiting managers for much pre-tender advice and peri-
odic site visits.

(4) Planning Engineer

To prepare the pre-contract programme assisted by the contracts
manager. An accurate assessment of the contract period is necessary as this is the time period on which resource allocations and
the contract preliminaries will be based.

Where the contract period is specified in the contract documents,
its feasibility should be checked. There are key areas on most
sites where congestion of activities may occur and a detailed
planning exercise may be required.

(5) Buyer

Firms vary widely in their purchasing procedures. Some highly
organised buying departments do not participate in estimating but
afford a service, once a contract is won and the documents are
received, which includes scheduling, progress chasing, works in-
spection and many other services. Other firms have a buyer who
undertakes tender enquiries and places covering orders when contracts are won, but leaves the scheduling and call up of materials
to site staff.

15

There is doubt about the practice of seeking quotations for tendering and then enquiring again if the contract is gained. If firms who quote know that their figure may be subject to 'Dutch auction' then they can be expected to add a margin. The objective of estimating is to arrive at a realistic and competitive net cost and such distortions are clearly unhelpful.

The buyer is normally responsible for preparing the enquiries for material suppliers and subcontractors at estimate stage. The enquiries must be sent out as early as possible in the estimate period to enable the firms to return the enquiries. The buyer will be responsible for comparing quotations received and passing the information to the job estimator for inclusion in the estimate build-up.

The comparison of quotations from suppliers and subcontractors may be compared on Form 3 as presented in the I.O.B. Code of Estimating Practice.[1]

(6) Office Manager

Responsible for co-ordinating the tender information. Document-ation produced throughout the tender will require collating for the tender adjudication meeting.

Quotations will be required for insurances and the provision of a contract bond where applicable. The assessment of the over-head percentage for the head office may also be the office manager's responsibility in conjunction with the accountant director.

(7) Job Estimator

Responsible for the build-up in net form of the rates for inclusion in the priced bill. The labour, plant and materials analysis of each rate may be indicated in order to assist analysis at the adjudication stage.

The job estimator will obtain materials quotations and may be advised by the chief estimator as to the responsibility of both these and the subcontractors' quotations, bearing in mind the experience of the firm concerned.

Labour constants are the means by which provision is made for the allowance for the work element, usually in the form of a factor applied to the billed quantity. They may be gained from published literature, often amended by experience. For some at least of the items however, it may be necessary to define method (plant and manning) more precisely, and in these cases the firm's resources of information (such as work study data and cost feedback data) may be called upon. Those firms with a well established comput-erised accounting system may develop an in-firm estimators' data bank, and, although the more significant items in the bill may be subject to a pricing exercise, a great many may then be printed in from that source.

16

Where a pricing exercise is required, the job estimator may well consult both the contracts manager (or prospective site manager) and the planner in order to be sure that his estimated cost represents their intentions.

In all cases a method statement outlining methods of construction is put to the adjudicating meeting.   Changes thus introduced may call for variation to the unit cost data.   Its direct function is to influence the provisions made in the contract preliminaries for plant and scaffolding, temporary roads and other items which are extra to provisions made in the bill rates of measured items.

The preliminaries build-up will be prepared in conjunction with the contracts manager and based on the contract period suggested by the planning department.

The chief estimator will co-ordinate the checking of the estimate and its presentation in summary form.

2.3 SITE VISIT REPORT INFORMATION

The preparation of a schedule of items is to be considered in order to prepare a site visit report and their effect on the contractor's bid is to be outlined.

2.3.1 Purpose of Report

The site visit report at tender stage is usually prepared by a representative of production management and the job estimator. It creates an understanding of conditions and restraints likely to have an influence on the works.   It also assists in the preparation of a list of questions to be put to designers, consultants and public undertakings in clarification of their requirements.

Code of Estimating Practice – Form 4[1] is designed for this purpose; it helps to ensure that no items are overlooked.

Contractors often develop their own site visit proforma to collect essential site information.

The site visit report should aim to collect the following data:

Item No.	Information required	Purpose/effect on bid
1	Ground conditions including type of ground, water table levels, extent of temporary support to be provided.	Affects methods of excavation, selection of plant, output of excavation plant and rates utilised for earth support. Provision of plant for pumping.
2	Location of tipping facilities, distance to tip, tipping fee.	Affects rates for disposal of excavated material.

Item No.	Information required	Purpose/effect on bid
3	Demolition of existing buildings.	These must be seen by the estimator in order that he may assess the cost of demolition and assess the extent of re-usable material or credits to be allowed for recovered material.
4	Access to site.	Affects extent of temporary roads to be provided in the contract preliminaries. Access difficulties for plant and vehicles must be noted. Phased deliveries of material may be necessary on site with limited access and storage facilities. Height and loading limits on bridges in the vicinity of the site are important.
5	Restrictions due to site location.	This will directly affect the location of storage facilities on site, extent of temporary hoardings or fencing to be provided. On restricted sites the location of offices may involve the provision of scaffold gantries.
6	Labour: items for consideration include (a) Availability of local tradesmen and labour. (b) Assessment of other major works in the neighbourhood and the likely effect on the contract. (c) Local rates of pay. (d) Availability of lodging facilities. (e) Transport to be provided for labour - catchment area for the contract.	Affects the build up of the all-in rate which will be affected by the plus rates payable in the area, extent of travelling time to be allowed in the rates or preliminaries. Degree of labour importation, provision of lodging facilities and allowances. Transportation of labour to site to be allowed in contract preliminaries.

Item No.	Information required	Purpose/effect on bid
7	Services: location of temporary water, electricity and telephone facilities. Location of foul and surface water services.	Monies to be allocated in contract preliminaries for temporary lighting, power supply for tower crane, etc. Temporary water service required for offices, labour, toilets and site mixing plant for concrete or bricklayers. Provision of temporary stand pipe/metered connection. Site toilets to be chemical type or connected to the foul sewer with a temporary connection.
8	Availability of local suppliers, subcontractors, plant and haulage facilities.	Affects the overall prices of subcontract work. The information is of use to the buying department at the enquiry stage. Hire rates for plant and haulage may be established locally at tender stage as these may differ from normal rates.
9	Site security.	Provision of site fencing, either to complete site boundary or to compound area only. The contract documents may specify protection of the public by using footpaths adjacent to the site, or the protection of personnel during alterations. The provision and extent of temporary dust screens will require assessment.
10	Other factors.	Topography of site in relation to ease and movement of plant.
		Extent of underground or overhead obstructions.
		Public transport services serving site.

It should be noted that much information about a site is only available from older sections of the local population whose memory reaches back to previous usage of the site. The possibility of mine shafts, old foundations, old water courses, filled ground, flooding and so on may not be obvious to a casual visitor. The nearest local authority yard and depot, as well as nearby residents, can be a fruitful source of cautionary information.

19

A site visit proforma, suitable for use in a contractor's organisation, is shown in Figure 2.3. Standard forms used in the estimating process enable comprehensive records to be built up for reference during the pre-contract period. The data collected during a site visit may vary from one firm to another, depending upon the nature of the work to be undertaken by the contractor, e.g. a piling subcontractor would be more concerned about the topography of the site and surface conditions likely to affect the movement of plant.

2.3.2 Example of a Completed Site Visit Report

A completed site visit report is given for a contract tender involving the construction of a new building located on an existing railway station platform.

Site Visit Report

Tender Number: 80/32   Date: 18 January 198-.

Contract: Preston Brook   Prepared by: A. Prichard

(1) Location of Site

The site is located within 800 m of the town centre and is approached by Rushton Street. Good major roads are within 1 km of the site with direct access from junction 26 of the M56.

Restricted parking facilities are in force at the front of the existing station and a large car-park for cars using the station is adjacent to the main entrance.

(2) Transport Services to Site

Adequate local bus services stop at the station. Key labour is to be imported from Manchester and it is anticipated that general labour can be recruited locally.

(3) Address of Job Centre

Job Centre located at 184 Hillgate, Preston Brook.
Tel. 061-794-2242. Manager - Mr. S. Brooks.
An adequate supply of general labour is currently on the books.

(4) Other Contracts in the Area

Three local authority housing contracts currently in progress within 5 km of the contract. Work on these projects is being undertaken by local contractors. No other national contractors working in the town.

```
┌─────────────────────────────────────────────────────────┐
│                    SITE VISIT REPORT                      │
├─────────────────────────────────────────────────────────┤
│                                                           │
│   TENDER NO.                    PREPARED BY               │
│                                                           │
│   CONTRACT                                                │
│                                                           │
│   DATE                                                    │
├─────────────────────────────────────────────────────────┤
│                                                           │
│                                   INFORMATION AVAILABLE   │
```

1   LOCATION OF SITE

2   TRANSPORT SERVICES TO SITE

3   ADDRESS OF JOB CENTRE

4   OTHER CONTRACTS IN AREA

5   ACCESS TO SITE

6   GROUND CONDITIONS ON SITE
     TOPOGRAPHY
     SURFACE WATER CONDITIONS

7   DETAILS OF TRIAL PITS AND
     WATER TABLE LEVELS

8   EXTENT OF TEMPORARY WORKS

9   AVAILABILITY OF LOCAL LABOUR

10   EXTENT OF SITE FENCING

11   SITE SECURITY AND LIGHTING

12   AVAILABILITY OF SUBCONTRACTORS

13   EXTENT OF WELFARE FACILITIES
     REQUIRED

14   TEMPORARY SERVICES TO BE
     PROVIDED

15   ANY SPECIAL REQUIREMENTS

Figure 2.3

21

(5) Access to Site

Access to the new station building is via the existing subway.
Excavated material from the foundations will have to be hand excavated and transported by dumper into the subway via the existing
station lift.   Skip containers to be located in disused end of
subway.

Concrete to the new platform foundations and slab can be pumped
from the rear subway access road direct into place.   Number of
visits to be assessed for the concrete pumping equipment.

Bricks to be double handled and transported by dumper or railway trolley via station parcels lift to platform level.   Bricks
to be handstacked on platform.

A large mobile crane will be required for the placing of the
precast beams.   This can be located on the existing station forecourt and the units raised over the existing forecourt wall.

(6) Ground Conditions

Excavate to platform bases in filled ground.   Shallow foundations
only.   No problems anticipated.

(7) Trial Pit Details and Water Table Levels

No information available.   No problems evident on site.

(8) Extent of Temporary Works

Metal decking required for subway drainage work to cover open
trenches.   Allow for 10 m of metal plates for protection and
cover.

Materials stacking area required for precast units on station
forecourt.   Area to be compounded at rear entrance to subway for
material storage area.

Platform bases when concreted to be temporarily filled in to
form level surface;   the station platform is in continuous passenger use during base construction.

(9) Availability of Local Labour

See note (3).   Up to six general labourers to be recruited ini-
tially.

(10) Extent of Site Fencing, Hoardings and Protection

Full extent indicated in bill - Reference 12/E F & G.

(i) Temporary staircase from subway - allow for removal and
re-erection twice during reconstruction of staircase.

(ii) Enclosed covered walkway to be allowed 2 m x 2.5 m by 10 m in length to provide protection to public. Walkways to be lighted at evenings.

(iii) Temporary chestnut fence to be erected around new platform works, approximate length 120 m, average 1.2 m high. Timber fender required in front of fence.

(iv) Existing subway area to be separately fenced off. Gates at rear entrance to be locked during evenings.

(11) Site Security

See item (10).

(12) Availability of Subcontractors and Merchants

Main domestic subcontractors to be engaged from Manchester.

> Plant Hire
>
> P & B Plant Hire   – Preston Brook 84312
> Morgans Haulage Co. – Preston Brook 72164
>
> Merchants
>
> Feb Industries   – Hollway 7213
> E. Bentley   – Acton 32179

(13) Welfare Facilities

Portaloo toilets to be erected in subway with temporary connection to sewer. British Rail to provide water supply. Canteen facilities available for operatives and staff in existing station buffet.

(14) Temporary Services

All temporary services available on existing platform.

(15) Demolitions

The front station wall is to be reduced 4 m in height and the existing stone coping taken down and refixed.

An independent scaffold will be required along the whole front elevation of the existing station – 80 m in length x 10 m in height.

Hand demolition to be allowed.

Crane required for handling existing stone copings – to be lowered to ground, stacked and refixed at lower level. Allow two visits for crane.

(16) Other Relevant Information

Permission to be obtained for track possession during the fixing of the precast beams to the new subway area. British Rail to provide watching and lookout facilities during craneage work.

All material storage areas on the existing platform to be securely fenced off.

2.4 OBJECTIVES OF METHOD STATEMENTS

An assessment of construction methods to be considered during tendering is required.

The objectives of preparing a method statement at the tender stage are to be indicated. A suitable format for the method statement is also to be shown.

2.4.1 Objectives of Preparing a Method Statement

(1) To enable managerial experience to be called upon during estimating, a demand is created for information relative to performance. Managers find it necessary to record resources, quantities and time in order to contribute.

(2) To enable data concerning new construction techniques and methods of handling materials to be included in an estimate. As the planning department is often consulted on method statements, a method statement may be developed from work study data and planning cycles prepared for alternative plant and labour situations.

(3) To permit the plant requirements for a project to be summarised for inclusion in the contract preliminaries or plant schedule.

(4) To ensure the output and duration of different methods and machines is realistically matched.

(5) To give guidance to the estimator on specific bill items relating to plant and labour requirements in order that realistic rates may be built up.

(6) To establish data relating to construction method but not finished work. This entails expense which is only recoverable by allowance in measured items or preliminaries. Scaffolding, materials handling and site installations are all affected.

Within organisations using centralised head office estimating, the regional office may be responsible for the preparation of the method statement for enquiries within its own region. The regional contracts manager will prepare the method statement and an assessment of contract preliminaries and submit these to the chief estimator for discussion at the main tender meeting.

24

When methods of construction have been agreed, the job estimator is responsible for interpreting the methods into realistic bill rates. Construction methods allowed in the estimate must be flexible enough to enable reconsideration at the pre-contract planning stage as more detailed information becomes available. Methods may, however, be changed, provided they fall within the budgeted cost for labour and plant. Where this is not possible a well documented contract may be able to establish a claim.

2.4.2 Format for Method Statements

Various formats for method statements are used by construction firms. These include a selection of the following

(1) A pre-printed format used for repetitive work of familiar design. This allows consideration of the number of gangs, number of standard units of shuttering, falsework and equipment, the plant requirement for siteworks, structural work and handling materials. The statement is prepared by the production team and also includes an assessment of the overall contract period.

(2) The method statement is shown in Figure 2.4. This can be used to indicate method and plant considerations which enable the quantity, output and operational duration to be assessed. The relationship between operations and the construction sequence can also be considered.

Alternative methods should, wherever possible, be considered on the method statement. Alternative durations may be offered for a range of differing gang sizes where the supply of skilled men is in doubt. Various examples of method statements prepared for a number of case studies are presented.

2.4.3 Information to be Included on Method Statements

(1) The operation or work stage

Each operation requiring analysis of plant or method should be listed in the method statement, e.g. excavation work, formwork operations where a choice of formwork systems or types of format is available and concrete handling and placing. Other operations include those involving the choice of plant for lifting precast floors or erecting steelwork.

(2) Quantity of work

This will directly affect methods of construction, number of machines to be selected and number of gangs to be employed.

(3) Methods of construction

Realistic methods together with constructive alternatives should be outlined. Discussion of the obvious does not assist the estimator in any way.

METHOD STATEMENT

CONTRACT:

TENDER NO:

SHEET NO:

PREPARED BY:

Operation Operation No.	Quantity	Method	Sequence of Operations	Plant & Labour	Output	Labour

Figure 2.4

(4) Sequence of operations

The sequence of operations should be indicated in order to outline
to the planner, estimator and construction manager alike the relationship and overlap between related operations.

(5) Plant summary

The summary of plant will assist in the preparation of the preliminaries plant element. N.B. Few items of plant operate inde-
pendently. Badly matched plant often restricts production. By
specifying alternative plant groupings rather than items, mistakes
may be avoided.

(6) Output

The anticipated output of an item of plant must be shown in order
that the duration for the plant may be assessed. From the output
and an assessment of the plant hire rates, the estimator may calculate unit rates for insertion in the bill.

(7) Duration

From the quantity and output the duration of the operation can be
assessed. The following technique may be applied in calculations
for items of plant.

$$\frac{\text{Quantity}}{\text{Output}} = \text{machine hours.} \qquad \frac{\text{Machine hours}}{\text{Hours worked per day}} = \text{machine days}$$

$$\frac{\text{Machine days}}{\text{No. of days per week}} = \text{machine weeks.} \qquad \frac{\text{Machine days/weeks}}{\text{No. of machines}} = \frac{\text{Duration in}}{\text{days or weeks}}$$

The same technique may be used to calculate the duration of a
trade gang.

$$\text{Quantity x target rate} = \text{man hours.} \qquad \frac{\text{Man hours}}{\text{Hours worked per day}} = \text{man days}$$

$$\frac{\text{Man days}}{\text{No. of days/week}} = \text{man weeks.} \qquad \frac{\text{Man days or man weeks}}{\text{Gang size}} = \frac{\text{Duration in gang days or gang weeks}}{}$$

2.5 EXAMPLES ON THE PREPARATION OF METHOD STATEMENTS

Example for Siteworks Project - City Site.

2.5.1 Contract Information

Reduced level excavation is to be carried out for a housing project. The area of the site on plan is 200 m by 150 m and an
average excavation depth of 0.50 m is to be carted off the site
to a nearby tip.

27

A method statement for the site reduced level excavation work is presented.

2.5.2 Assumptions Based on Site Visit Report

(1) Good access to site by means of existing streets which should be left in position until the excavation work is complete.

(2) Local authority tipping facilities located 3 km from the site. Tipping fee £1.00 per load.

(3) Surface material to be excavated consists of filling material remaining from demolished properties. A number of cellars are apparent on the block plans for the site. The existing site is reasonably level.

2.5.3 Method Considerations

Method 1. Use of a crawler tractor, hydraulic power shovel with a 1.5 m^3 capacity bucket. A number of machines are to be used loading 8 to 10 m^3 capacity tipping lorries (Figure 2.5).

Alternative Methods

Method 2. Use of tracked hydraulic excavator fitted with back-actor arm. Excavator fitted with wide 1 m^3 capacity bucket. Excavator to load lorries direct (Figure 2.6)

Method 3. Use of D6 bulldozer to excavate and push the material into spoil heaps adjacent to the access roads. Excavate using draglines located on top of spoil heaps and load tipping lorries direct. Two draglines to be utilised (Figure 2.7).

Notes on selection of methods of construction and plant selection.

Methods proposed must be realistic and based on the sound practical experience of production management. Site access, surface conditions and the type of soil being excavated will greatly affect the output of the plant.

Example for the Construction of a Reinforced Concrete Culvert

2.5.4 Contract Information

An assessment of the construction methods is required for the construction of a reinforced concrete box culvert. Refer to plan and section indicated in Figure 2.8.

Ground conditions from the site investigation report indicate a firm dry soil to a depth of 6 m with no apparent ground-water problems.

Method 1. - Hydraulic power shovel loading wagons direct

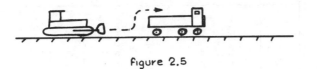

figure 2.5

Method 2 - Hydraulic backactor loading wagons direct

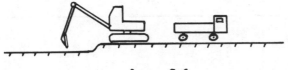

figure 2.6

Method 3 - Bulldozer pushing material into spoil heaps

spoil
heaps

Re-excavate at spoil heaps with dragline and
load wagons

Figure 2.7

METHOD STATEMENT

CONTRACT: HIGHER HILLGATE

TENDER NO: 79/46

SHEET NO: 1

PREPARED BY: B.C.

OPER-ATION NO.	OPERATION	QUANTITY	METHOD	SEQUENCE OF OPERATIONS	PLANT & LABOUR	OUTPUT	DURATION
1	Excavate to reduced levels (0.500 m deep)	200 x 150 x 0.5 = 15000 m^3	2 D6 Bulldozers to excavate and push the material into spoil heaps adjacent to the access roads. 2 Draglines fitted with 2 m^3 buckets to be located on top of each spoil heap. Lorries to use existing roads for access for loading.	Level grid to be established prior to excavation	2 D6 Dozers	120 m^3/h per machine = 2 x 120 = 240 m^3/h	$\frac{15000}{240}$ = $\frac{62.5}{8}$ h = 8 machine days
					1 Banksman		
					2 Draglines	75 m^3/h	$\frac{15000}{150}$
					4 Lorries per machine	= 75 x 2 = 150 m^3/h	= $\frac{100}{8}$ h = 12 machine days

30

METHOD STATEMENT

CONTRACT: HIGHER HILLGATE

TENDER NO: 79/46

SHEET NO: 2

PREPARED BY: B.C.

OPER-ATION NO.	OPERATION	QUANTITY	METHOD	SEQUENCE OF OPERATIONS	PLANT & LABOUR	OUTPUT	DURATION
1	ALTERNATIVE Excavate to reduced levels	15000 m^3	3 Hydraulic tracked excavators fitted with backactor arm. Machine to be fitted with 1½ m^3 bucket. Load lorries direct and remove to tip off site. Note on output – in relation to lorries conveying excavated material to tip. Machine output 45 m^3 per hour. Time taken to load 9 m^3 capacity lorry $\frac{9}{45}$ x 60 min = 12 min Travel to tip and return allow 24 min $\therefore \frac{24}{12}$ = 2 lorries + 1 = 3 lorries required for balance $\therefore$ 3 lorries per machine to be provided	Level grid to be established prior to exca-vation	3 Hydraulic excavators 3 Lorries per machine 1 Banksman	45 m^3/h 45 x 3 = 135 m^3/h	$\frac{15000}{135}$ $= \frac{112}{8}$ h = 14 machine days

31

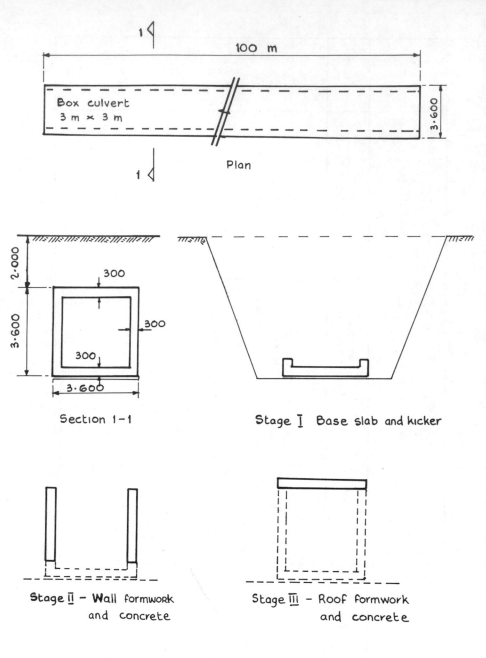

100 m

Box culvert
3 m × 3 m

3·600

Plan

2·000

300

300

3·600

300

3·600

Section 1-1

Stage I Base slab and kicker

Stage II – Wall formwork
and concrete

Stage III – Roof formwork
and concrete

Sequence of Construction for Reinforced
Concrete Culvert

Figure 2.8

32

2.5.5 Operations to be Considered

   (1) Excavate to culvert
   (2) Earth support to excavations
   (3) Concrete blinding to base slab
   (4) Formwork and reinforcement to base slab
   (5) Concrete base slab
   (6) Formwork and reinforcement to walls
   (7) Concrete to walls
   (8) Formwork and reinforcement to roof slab
   (9) Concrete to roof slab
  (10) Backfill to culvert

2.5.6 Initial Considerations - Construction Sequence

(1) Excavate to Culvert

Depth of excavation 5.600 m. Site report indicates good ground conditions therefore consider a battered excavation. Consider lowering ground level approximately 1 m to reduce digging depth of machine.

Hydraulic tracked excavator with backactor arm - Rushton Bucyrus 90H or similar machine loading 8 m^3 capacity waggons and part remove to tip off site.

(2) Earth Support to Excavations

Battered excavation - allow 4 m additional width of excavation at existing ground level - cost of additional excavation and backfill to be considered as part of earthwork support rate in the bill.

(3) Concrete Blinding to Base

Blinding to be undertaken in 20 m bays as excavation work proceeds.

(4) Formwork and Reinforcement to Base - Stage 1

Base slab to be constructed in 10 m floor bays. Edge formwork to be constructed of standard plywood panel shutters with suspended 150 mm high kicker to walls. Reinforcement to floor bays may precede formwork to base. Low pivot job crane to be used for lowering reinforcement into culvert.

(5) Concrete Base Slab

Low pivot jib crane and skips to be used for lowering ready mixed concrete into culvert base. The crane will also be required for handling the reinforcement and formwork to the walls.

(6) Formwork and Reinforcement to Walls - Stage 2

Both walls to be erected to full height, e.g. to underside of roof slab. Patent strongback formwork to be used with plywood facing. Wall formwork to be erected in 10 m panels. Mobile, low pivot jib crane to be used for handling formwork.   Allow for part remake of wall formwork after 8 uses.   Reinforcement to walls may progress ahead of wall formwork.

(7)   Concrete to Walls

As for ground floor slab pour - use of crane and skips in conjunction with ready mixed concrete supply.

(8)   Formwork and Reinforcement to Roof Slab - Stage 3

Formwork roof supports to be rawl bolted to concrete walls. Patent steel roof supports to be used in connection with plywood soffit panels.   Delay on striking time will affect number of formwork uses.   Allow for 3 uses of roof soffit.

(9)   Concrete to Roof Slab

Use of crane and skips as before.

(10)   Backfill to Culvert

On completion of concreting to the roof slab and the striking of all formwork, backfilling may be undertaken using an hydraulic power shovel fitted with a four in one bucket.

Example of Factory Project

2.5.7   Contract Information

A contractor has received an enquiry for the construction of a factory unit.   Scheme plans and elevations are shown in Figure 2.9.

   The preparation of a method statement for the contract is based on the following operations.

2.5.8   Operations to be Considered

(1)   Excavate to reduced level and remove to tip
(2)   Excavate and concrete work to pad foundations
(3)   Erect steelwork and roof sheeting
(4)   Hardcore to ground floor slab
(5)   Concrete ground floor slab
(6)   External brickwork
(7)   Drainage work and sewer connection

2.5.9   Information Obtained from Site Visit Report

Concrete to be supplied to the project ready mixed.

   Erection of steelwork and roof sheeting to be carried out by a nominated subcontractor.

34

Method Statement for Factory Project

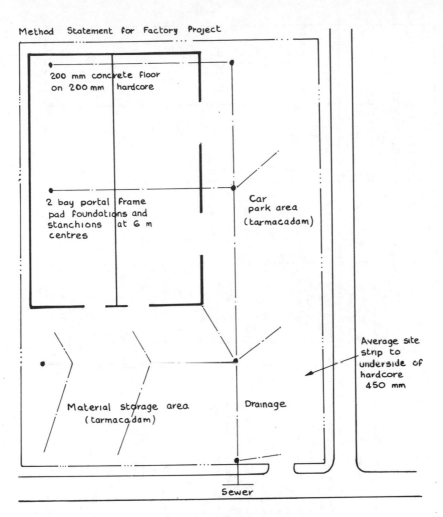

200 mm concrete floor
on 200 mm hardcore

2 bay portal frame
pad foundations and
stanchions at 6 m
centres

Car
park area
(tarmacadam)

Average site
strip to
underside of
hardcore
450 mm

Material storage area
(tarmacadam)

Drainage

Sewer

Plan of Factory Unit

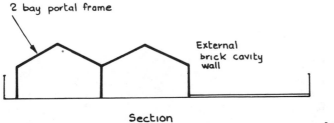

2 bay portal frame

External
brick cavity
wall

Section

Scale 1: 500

figure 2.9

METHOD STATEMENT

CONTRACT: FACTORY UNIT
TENDER NO: 81/22

SHEET NO: 1
PREPARED BY: B.C.
DATE: 20.1.81

OPER-ATION NO.	OPERATION	QUANTITY	METHOD	SEQUENCE OF OPERATIONS	PLANT & LABOUR	OUTPUT	DURATION
1	Excavate oversite to reduce levels and remove to tip	70 m x 100 m x ave. 450 mm = 3150 m³	Excavate using hydraulic power shovels (Cat.951 or similar). Load excavated material direct into 8 m³ capacity lorries and cart away to tip. Alternative. Excavate using hydraulic backbactor, track mounted 360° slewing machine loading direct into lorries Hymac 580 or similar	Site strip to commence after taking initial grid of levels / Ditto	1 Banksman, Cat.951 Crawler tractor, 4 lorries / 1 Banksman	40 m³/h / 35 m³/h	$= \frac{3150}{40}$ = 79 man-h $= \frac{79}{9}$ h/day / $= \frac{3150}{35}$ = 90 man-h $= \frac{90}{9}$ = 10 days
2	Excavate pad and strip foundations	300 mm of strip fdn 40 pad fdn bases Say 200 m³	Excavate shallow foundations using Hymac 580 as before and load direct into lorries. Alternative. Use wheeled multipurpose excavator JCB 4C or similar	On stripping factory area the excavation work to the factory area may commence. Temporary access, hardcored road required for vehicular access to excavator	1 Banksman, 1 Hymac, 2 Lorries / 1 JCB 4C, 2 Lorries		Allow 5 days

36

METHOD STATEMENT

CONTRACT: FACTORY UNIT
TENDER NO: 81/22

SHEET NO: 2
PREPARED BY: B.C.
DATE: 20.1.81

OPER-ATION NO.	OPERATION	QUANTITY	METHOD	SEQUENCE OF OPERATIONS	PLANT & LABOUR	OUTPUT	DURATION
3	Concrete strip and pad foundations	100 m^3 Ready mixed concrete	Ready mixed concrete to be discharged direct into foundations. Site access via hardcored formation. Alternative. Ready mixed concrete to be transported via dumper fitted with turntable skip	On fixing of bolt boxes to 6 pad foundations, concrete work may commence	3 Labourers	–	1 day/ 4 to 6 bases
4	Erect steelwork and roof cladding	N/S/C	Contractor to prepare central area of floor slabs with oversite hardcore for crane during erection. Erect steelwork with a low pivot jib crane or alternatively telescopic jib crane lorry mounted	Bases to be checked by steelwork contractor prior to erection, and levelling of bases to receive steelwork. Bases to one bay of portal to be complete prior to erection of steelwork	N/S/C	–	10 days

CONTRACT: FACTORY UNIT
TENDER NO: 81/22

METHOD STATEMENT

SHEET NO: 3
PREPARED BY: B.C.
DATE: 20.1.81

OPER-ATION NO.	OPERATION	QUANTITY	METHOD	SEQUENCE OF OPERATIONS	PLANT & LABOUR	OUTPUT	DURATION
5	Lay 200 mm hardcore bed and concrete ground floor slab	$7000\ m^2$	Limestone bed 200 mm thick to be tipped spread and level with crawler tractor fitted with 4 in 1 bucket. Compact with tandem vibrating roller	Drainage work	Crawler tractor BTD100. 1 Banksman. Vibrating roller	$100\ m^3/h$ $= \dfrac{7000}{100}$ $= \dfrac{70}{9}$ man-h	$= 8$ machine days
	Concrete G.F. slab	$7000\ m^2$ (Bay size 6 m x 50 m) $= 60\ m^3/\text{bay}$	Direct access to be maintained for R.M. concrete wagons. Floor to be divided into 6 m wide bays. Continuous bay construction to be used leaving access bay for infill. Finish with vibrating screed board	Metal road forms to be laid in advance of slab construction. Concrete floor to commence on completion of roof sheeting	1 Vibrating screed. 2 Labrs placing. 2 Labrs finishing. 2 Labrs covering	2 floor bays per day using 1 gang/bay	$\dfrac{24}{2}$ bays $= 12$ days
6	Brickwork to external walls	180 x 6 m.ht. $= 1080\ m^2$ $= 1080\ x\ 120$ $= 129600$ bricks	Fork lift truck to be used for all brick handling. Allow 2 gangs of bricklayers. Total bricklayer strength to be 6 B/L and 4 labourers. Mortar to be mixed on site and handled with fork lift truck. External scaffold access to walls	Brickwork operation to follow erection of steel frame and associated lining and plumbing	2 B/L mixers. 1 Fork lift truck. Scaffolding	800 bricks per day per bricklayer	$\dfrac{129600}{800}$ $= 162$ man days $= \dfrac{162}{5} = 32$ man weeks $= \dfrac{32}{6}$ say 6 weeks duration

38

Good access to the site from adjacent roadways. The factory project forms part of a new industrial estate and the site roads have been constructed.

2.6 SOURCES OF ESTIMATING INFORMATION

The sources of information available to an estimator in order to establish bill rates are

(1) Labour outputs and constants
(2) Plant rates and outputs
(3) Material prices
(4) Quotations for subcontract work

2.6.1 Information Sources Available

Figure 2.10 summarises the main sources of information available on labour, materials and plant. Many of these sources are notoriously imprecise and a great deal of experience is necessary when comparing information from different sources.

Output figures for labour may be gained from work study, by cost checks on actual site operations over a period of time, and from builders' price books. These outputs are collected for different purposes and allow for different contingency amounts. They are somewhat affected by site conditions, access problems and the weather. The amount of contract supervision and provision of resources at the work face will directly affect the results. Analysis of data collected rarely supplies information on these factors.

2.6.2 Sources of Data on Labour Outputs

The firm has to decide first of all if its labour constants are genuinely a man hour allowance (quantity related) which can be included knowing that provision will later be introduced for materials, plant and overheads. The Code of Estimating Practice (5.061) recommends the utilisation of elemental analysis in order that each element (labour, materials and plant) is estimated separately. The necessity for an item to be precisely estimated is less important than that it should afford an equitable basis for negotiating alterations and additions (if required) and that the sum of timesing out and summing all such items should bring the total to a workable and competitive amount.

Research by Mannerings[4] showed that only 10% to 15% of the rates used in a tender build-up directly affected the competitiveness of the bid. This implies that the estimator is better concentrating his efforts on key bill items which directly affect the end result rather than building up labour targets for every bill item in every trade. The use of a data bank of target rates or a comprehensive schedule of outputs covering common bill items would aid the estimating process and allow the estimator to consider more closely the key operations. In this way target rates

39

SOURCES OF ESTIMATING DATA

LABOUR ——————

- EXPERIENCE OF THE ESTIMATOR
- COMPANY LABOUR TARGET SCHEDULES
- WORK STUDY DATA
- RANDOM COST, FEEDBACK DATA
- BONUS TARGETS
- PUBLISHED OUTPUT DATA –
    SPONS, HUTCHINS AND LAXTONS
- TRADE JOURNALS – BUILDING,
    ARCHITECTS' JOURNAL AND Q.S.WEEKLY
- ANALYSIS OF BONUS DATA
- LABOUR ONLY QUOTATIONS

MATERIALS ——————

- CURRENT QUOTATIONS
- PREVIOUS QUOTATIONS UPDATED
- MANUFACTURERS' PRICE LISTS
- PUBLISHED MATERIAL PRICES – SPONS,
    LAXTONS, BUILDING TRADES JOURNAL,
    BUILDING
- BUYING DEPARTMENT RECORDS

PLANT ——————

- EXPERIENCE OF ESTIMATOR
- PLANT OUTPUTS FROM PLANT RECORDS
- RANDOM OBSERVATIONS, FEEDBACK
- MANUFACTURERS' DATA – REPORTS
- TRADE JOURNALS – ARTICLES AND REPORTS
- WORK STUDY OBSERVATIONS
- EXPERIENCE DRAWN FROM CONSTRUCTION
- MANAGEMENT

Figure 2.10

40

for key bill items must be more closely related to methods analysis.

Clearly the more closely price and cost are related to the level of individual items, the lower the element of risk involved. Nevertheless to establish a data processing system for a contractor to obtain for a high degree of accuracy involves considerable cost and careful design of the control and accounting systems.

Some estimators (probably the majority) continue to use price book type labour constants, which, in effect, add an effort factor allowing generously for contingencies and little else. On the other hand, some companies are now providing labour constants from a detailed data bank. These latter are subject to errors of input and interpretation and variations in data collected under a single heading may not be explained. Such systems should then offer statistical parameters of central tendency and distribution so that they can be applied intelligently.

2.6.3 Sources of Data on Plant Outputs

Similar conditions apply to the estimated and recorded output of plant. Machines are being continually developed and thus performance can only be related to a specific model. Conditions vary from site to site and the selection of the most suitable plant is subject to great risks of uncertainty in the conditions of work. (Reference Code of Estimating Practice 5.081). Hence plant selection must be based on the consideration of realistic alternatives by means of a method statement. Advice at estimate stage must be sought from production management. Few plant managers seek out data about production output; indeed this varies significantly with the operator, associated equipment and transport, access conditions and the progress rate of the job. Plant cost is time related and its relationship to quantity is complex.

A hire rate can be expressed in machine hour units which can be directly related to an output assessment based on the site task and conditions. This price can be estimated, plus the effort involved in the organisation of the plant. The additional cost of its delivery and removal from site can be adequately covered in the preliminaries assessment.

A large proportion of bill items are insignificant in terms of the financial performance of a contract. To treat them in detail entails cost in data collection and processing which may offer little benefit.

2.6.4 Sources of Data on Materials

Material costs which are not catered for by quotation are matters of cutting, waste, compaction and losses arising from site management and security. Allowances must also be made for unloading, handling, storing and packaging. It is clear that unacceptable losses must be investigated, but some percentage allowance which is periodically checked against experience is all the provision available to the estimator.

2.7 OBTAINING QUOTATIONS FROM SUBCONTRACTORS AND SUPPLIERS

The Institute of Building Code of Estimating Practice deals with
the detailed preparation of the estimate in relation to the build-
up of unit rates.   An essential pre-requisite is the sending
out of enquiries for materials and subcontractors.

2.7.1 Material Enquiries

This will involve preparing a schedule of material for which
enquiries are to be sent out.   It will first be necessary to
obtain quantities for each material which may be abstracted from
the bills of quantities or approximated from the tender drawings.

Enquiries should embody all relevant information to enable
accurate quotations to be submitted.   They should state the
terms and conditions upon which the quotations are to be based.
In the majority of cases the material enquiry is photostatted
from the tender documents, e.g. the relevant pages of the bills
of quantities and specification.   A brief summary of the contract
particulars may also be sent in the form of a standard enquiry
letter.

Appendix A of the Code of Estimating Practice outlines the
information to be given in enquiries to suppliers.   This indicates that the enquiry should state

(1) The specification of the material
(2) Quantity of material
(3) The likely delivery programme
(4) Address of the site
(5) Means of access
(6) Any traffic conditions and restrictions affecting delivery
(7) Period for which the quotation is required to remain open
     for acceptance
(8) Date by which quotation is to be submitted
(9) The person in the main contractor's organisation to whom
     reference concerning the enquiry should be made.

A list of firms to whom the enquiry is to be sent must be
established.   The firm's policy may dictate the number of enquiries to be sent out which may be based on a selected list of
suppliers.   A model form suitable for abstracting data for material enquiries is indicated in the Estimating Code of Practice
(Form E/ME/2).

2.7.2 Receipt of Material Quotations

Quotations in answer to enquiries must be compared and a quotation
selected for use in the calculation of the rate.   Quotations may
be compared by tabulating the terms of competing quotations in
order that a sound choice may be made.   Model form E/SQ/6 in the
Estimating Code of Practice may be used for this purpose.

The Institute of Building, Estimating Information Service Paper No.19 entitled 'Suppliers Invitation to Tender for the Supply of Materials'[5] outlines the supplier's problems in dealing with enquiries.

2.7.3 Subcontractors' Enquiries

Examination of the drawings and bills of quantities will establish the extent of work to be sublet.   Decisions will have to be made relating to the number of trade enquiries to be sent out for each subcontract in order that competitive bids may be obtained.   The contractor may adopt a policy of sharing the subcontract workload in one area between three or four reliable subcontractors in preference to setting up a 'Dutch auction' for every tender enquiry. In this way a good working relationship may be established between the main contractor and his subcontractors.

Where tenders are being prepared for contracts in new work areas, information regarding the availability of subcontractors may be collected as part of the site visit report.

Appendix A of the Code of Estimating Practice outlines the information to be given in enquiries to subcontractors and indicates that the enquiry should state

(1)   Quantity of work extracted from the bills and any relevant specification clauses

(2)   Whether the quotation is to be for labour only or for labour and material

(3)   Plant and equipment to be provided by the main contractor and what the subcontractor will have to supply for himself

(4)   Anticipated commencement and completion dates for the subcontract work, work programme and sequences

(5)   Brief description of the proposed structure

(6)   Address of site

(7)   Name of client

(8)   Names and addresses of architect, quantity surveyor, and, when applicable, consulting engineers

(9)   Form of contract under which the sub-contract would be executed

(10)   Relevant information from the Appendix to the main contract

(11)   Any general conditions, specification or drawings to which the subcontractor would be required to adhere

(12) Address and times at which all documents could be inspected

(13) Whether a fixed or variable price sub-contract

(14) Terms of payment to the subcontractor

(15) A statement that the conditions of the enquiry would automatically form part of any sub-contract entered into

(16) Period for which the quotation is required to remain open for acceptance

(17) Date by which quotation should be submitted

(18) The person in the main contractor's organisation to whom reference concerning the enquiry should be made

2.7.4 The Receipt of Subcontractors' Enquiries

Quotations received must be compared and for this purpose the summary of subcontractors' quotations, Form E/SCQ/7, in the Code of Estimating Practice may be used. This enables net quotations to be compared after adjusting for discounts. The estimator must check when comparing quotations that

(1) The quotation complies with the bill of quantities and specifications
(2) The unit rates are consistent throughout the quotation
(3) The rates are realistic and comparable with competitors
(4) The quotation includes for preliminaries and attendances
(5) The quotation complies with the terms of the main contract regarding the payment period, retention and defects liability
(6) There are no onerous conditions attached to the subcontract

It is usual to include a percentage addition on a subcontractor's selected quotation to cover for any items which are likely to attract cost. These include items such as

(1) Unloading subcontractor's goods
(2) The protection and security of material
(3) Provision of storage facilities
(4) Provision of plant and the use of scaffolding
(5) The use of power
(6) Protection of the finished work

A further percentage is added to the subcontractor's quotation to include for the contractor's profit and risk element.

2.7.5 The Build-up of Unit Rates

In the majority of large organisations rates are built up in unit
rate form based on the net cost of labour, materials and plant,
and exclusive of any overhead addition. This enables the contractor to assess the net value of the total estimate at the
tendering stage. The net cost values may later form the basis
of the control system to be adopted by the contractor during the
project.

Allowances must be made to the materials element for waste and
consolidation factors. Further adjustments may be necessary for
cost increases due to the delivery of small quantities of material,
e.g. surcharges on concrete deliveries.

Sources of estimating information on labour, materials and
plant are outlined in section 2.6 of the text.

2.8 BUILD-UP OF THE ESTIMATE

A contractor has received an enquiry for a factory project and
he is keen to submit a competitive bid.

The documents on which the estimate is to be based consist
of contract drawings, specification and a schedule of P.C. sums
to be included in the estimate.

Outline the procedures to be undertaken during the build-up
of the estimate in net rate form.

2.8.1 Procedure During the Build-up of the Estimate Net Rates

(1) The drawings will be carefully analysed and a direct
bill of quantities prepared in trade order or elements. Careful
consideration of the specification requirements and of details
shown on available working drawings will require matching in order
to raise queries with the architect or client.

(2) The site will be visited by the job estimator and a manager, and a site visit report prepared of items likely to affect
the contractor's preliminaries.

(3) Enquiries will be sent out to the domestic subcontractors
where appropriate.

(4) Enquiries will be sent out to suppliers.

(5) Quotations will be scheduled and evaluated for inclusion.

(6) The net estimate build-up in labour, material and plant
form will be undertaken and analysed in columns adjacent to the
relevant direct bill item. In this way the taking off and estimate build-up can be carefully matched for anomalies.

(7) Rates will be built up in analytical form in order to provide an analysis for management. Labour constants based on the experience of the estimator or from historical cost data will be applied to a build-up of the 'All-in Rate' for craft operatives and labourers. Plant outputs will be based on a schedule of plant constants or the estimator's experience as discussed and material will be evaluated from quotations received.

(8) Built up net rate totals will then be entered into the unit rate column for the appropriate bill description and extended into cash and totalled on each page. The extended totals of labour, plant and materials can be checked against the cash total.

A build-up of the 'All-in Rate' for craft operatives and labourers is shown in Figure 2.11.

This format of presentation provides an analytical analysis in net form to be presented directly adjacent to the measured quantities.

2.8.2 Preliminaries Build-up

A draft bill of preliminary items will be built up in sufficient detail to adquately cover the site requirements. Advice on the extent of plant to be included will be obtained from the production section. A careful assessment of the attendances to be provided for nominated subcontractors will need to be made together with the necessary full price allowance.

2.8.3 Estimate Summary

On compilation of the estimate a summary of the estimate content will be prepared in order to assist management adjudication. The points to be considered at the adjudication meeting are outlined in section 2.10.

2.8.4 Calculation of All-in Hourly Rate for Craft Operative and Labourer

The build up of the 'All-in Rate' is based upon the wage agreement promulgated on 24 June 1991 which came into effect on 30 June 1991. Wage agreements for the building industry for a 39-hour week are based on

         Craftsman £139.03   Rate per hour £3.56
         Labourer £118.36   Rate per hour £3.03

The Chartered Institute of Building Code of Estimating Practice Section 7.03 indicates a further detailed analysis of the 'All-in Rate' assessment.

46

Basic Rate   Date 24-6-91

			Craftsman Labourer	Basic	Bonus
				139.03	16.57
				118.36	14.23
Working hours per annum	52 weeks	39 hours	2028		
Annual holiday	21 days	8 hours			
Public holidays	4 days	8 hours	168		
	3 days	9 hours	32		
			27		
			227 227		

Total hours per annum   1801

Weekly Earnings

	Craftsman		Labourer	
		£		£
Number of weeks	46.18 at £155.90	7199.46	at £132.59	6123.00
National Insurance	11%	791.94		673.53
CITB levy	sum	80.00		60.00
Plus rate allowance	average at 40 pence/hr	720.40	at 15 pence/hr	270.15
Tool allowance	at 10 pence/hr	180.10		
Annual holiday	46.18 weeks at £18.00	831.24		831.24
Total pay per annum		9803.14		7957.92

Craftsman's rate   = £5.44 per hour   = £4.42 per hour
- by 1801   Labourer rate

Figure 2.11

The calculation is based on 1801 average hours per year, which results in a calculated 'All-in Rate' of

Craft Operative $\dfrac{9803.14}{1801}$ = £5.44 per hour

Labourer $\dfrac{7957.92}{1801}$ = £4.42 per hour

2.9 BUILD-UP OF CONTRACT PRELIMINARIES OR PROJECT OVERHEADS

A contractor has received an enquiry for the construction of a five-storey office block located on an industrial park. The items of preliminaries to be considered at the estimate stage are shown and presented in the form of a check list.

Contract Information

Site located 20 km from the main contractor's office
Planner's assessment of contract period - 48 weeks
The frame of the building is of reinforced concrete
Approximate contract value £1,480,000

2.9.1 Procedures to be Observed

A site visit will be undertaken and a report prepared. It is essential for the estimator to visit the site in order to assess the provision of temporary work. The preliminaries will be directly affected by items such as site access, the location of adjacent buildings, and the extent of demolition work to be carried out. The estimator will seek managerial advice in relation to the construction method and the selection of major items of plant. Reference will be made to the method statement prepared by the Contracts Manager or planning section.

2.9.2 Presentation of Contract Preliminaries

The contract documents (Bills of Quantities - preliminaries section, Specification) must be reviewed in detail so that the estimator understands the contract requirements. Examination of the drawings will be necessary if they are not contained within the contract documents.

Many bills of quantities contain standard preliminary clauses with which the estimator will often be quite familiar. Where a specification is provided in lieu of a bill of quantities a full list of preliminary items relevant to the particular project will have to be drawn up. The estimator must decide which items of the preliminaries are to be fully priced up, because an over-estimation at this stage may easily result in a non-competitive bid. Some agreement must be reached with operational management regarding the provisions for temporary services, hoardings, hardstandings, access requirements and other items directly associated with the construction methods to be utilised.

48

Reference to the pre-tender programme and method statements will enable durations to be assessed for staffing and major items of plant.

The monetary sum included for preliminaries has a direct relationship to the assessed contract period; hence a reduction in the assessed contract period will have a corresponding effect on the preliminaries and thus the competitiveness of the overall bid.   It is essential that due consideration be given to the pre-tender planning procedures - one should not simply accept the contract period stated in the documents.   A tender built up based on a shorter contract period will directly affect monies included for staffing and accommodation and thus provide the final competit-ive edge to the contractor's bid.

In certain instances, experience has shown that some companies have a policy of 'only pricing preliminary items on which they are likely to incur a cost'.   Analysis of monies expended on prelim-inary items may be assessed from cost feedback information as part of a company's budgetary control procedures.   This practice may prove to be a more competitive approach to the pricing of pre-liminaries.

The preliminary items which are normally given consideration in pricing on a contract include

  (1) Site staffing
  (2) Cleaning site and clearing rubbish
       Note: Subcontractors should be made responsible for
       their own site clearance on completion of their work
  (3) Site transport facilities
  (4) Mechanical plant and hoisting
  (5) Scaffolding and gantries
  (6) Site accommodation
  (7) Small tools
  (8) Temporary services and reinstatement
  (9) Public services - electricity, telephone fees and rates
 (10) Temporary water installation
 (11) Welfare and safety provisions
 (12) Defects liability costs
 (13) Final clean out of building
 (14) Transport of operatives
 (15) Abnormal overtime
 (16) Setting out the works, including equipment
 (17) Samples and testing
 (18) Attendances on subcontractors and suppliers
 (19) Insurance for the works
 (20) Fixed price allowances (or anywhere additional monies may
       be concealed).

The following preliminary items are directly affected by the location of the site and conditions prevailing at the time of the tender

(1)   Travelling expenses for operatives
(2)   Labour importation costs - subsistence allowances
(3)   Access problems associated with undertaking the works - provision of covered access ways, temporary roads etc.
(4)   Hardstandings for plant, special work in connection with tower crane tracks
(5)   Protection of the public and building users, if applicable.   Check references in preliminary clauses to the provision of hoardings, fencing off work areas etc.

The cost of many of the preliminary items will vary in direct proportion to the contract period.   It is normal for costs to be built up on a fixed-charge basis and a time-related basis.

The Chartered Institute of Building Code of Estimating Practice (6th Edition), section 9.04 sets out a series of proformas for pricing project overheads (preliminaries).   Each section of the preliminaries is considered in relation to 'fixed costs' and 'time-related costs'.

Examples of fixed and time-related items are

        Site accommodation
        Fixed cost element - Bringing cabins to site
                             Erection of cabins
                             Fitting out and decoration
                             Furniture and fittings
                             Services to site cabins
                             Dismantle on completion
                             Return of cabins to stores

        Site accommodation
        Time-related costs - Number of cabins required
                             to suit contractor's needs   Ref.A.
                             Servicing of accommodation   cost/
                             Rates   week

                           - Cost/week times number of weeks
                             allocated to the project

Note
The contractor's quantity surveyor may be required to submit to the client's quantity surveyor a build up of the preliminaries costs in order that they may be fairly apportioned at each valuation stage.
(P.S. At this stage the contractor is trying to convince the client's quantity surveyor that he has £10,000 in the preliminaries as a fixed cost for mobilising the site set up - if only he could get away with it!)

Temporary Works Fixed cost element		Temporary Works Time-related costs
Access roads	- Provision Removal Making good	Maintenance Cleaning
Hardstandings	- Provision Removal Making good	Maintenance Cleaning
Pumping and Dewatering	- Installation Adaptation Removal	Attendant labour Servicing

Refer to CIOB Code of Estimating Practice (6th Edition), pages 97 to 107 for proforma layouts.

The monetary value of the preliminaries must in some way allow for an element of risk. Contractors may often use the preliminaries section of the bill to 'hide' monies for certain risk items.

2.9.3 Preliminaries Build-Up

In relation to the five-storey office project, the pricing of a number of preliminary items, together with a range of proformas, will be illustrated.

Figure 2.12a illustrates a proforma indicating a summary of contract preliminaries. The layout is divided into time-related and fixed cost sections.

Figure 2.12b indicates the pricing of time-related items with reference to Employers' Requirements, i.e. accommodation/telephones/testing and equipment.

Figure 2.12c indicates the pricing of fixed cost items relative to Employers' Requirements.

The preliminaries monetary value, when totalled, may be expressed in percentage form for comparisons between estimate submissions. In practice, the preliminaries percentage varies widely - say between 2% and 15% of the contract sum. This wide variation is due to the apportionment of the contractor's overheads and profit, since part of it may be included in the preliminaries. The CIOB Code of Practice outlines ways of apportioning profit at the adjudication stage.

```
┌──────────────────────────────────────────────────────────────────┐
│ CONTRACT:  5 Storey Office Block           TENDER REF:   90/53     │
│ CONTRACT PERIOD:  45 weeks                                         │
│ TENDER ALL-IN RATES  -  TRADESMAN:            LABOURER:            │
│ TENDER SUBMISSION DATE:  15 Oct. 1991                             │
├──────────────────────────────────────────────────────────────────┤
│               SUMMARY OF CONTRACT PRELIMINARIES                   │
├──────────────────────────────┬───────────────────────────────────┤
│ A - TIME-RELATED COSTS       │ LABOUR  PLANT  MATERIAL  S/C  TOTAL│
│                              │                                   │
│  1 Employer's requirements   │                                   │
│  2 Site staffing             │                                   │
│  3 Site accommodation        │                                   │
│  4 Attendant labour          │                                   │
│  5 Miscellaneous labour costs│                                   │
│  6 Facilities and services   │                                   │
│  7 Temporary works           │                                   │
│  8 Mechanical plant          │                                   │
│  9 Non-mechanical plant      │                                   │
│ 10 Sundry items              │                                   │
├──────────────────────────────┴───────────────────────────────────┤
│                            TOTAL                                  │
├──────────────────────────────┬───────────────────────────────────┤
│ B - FIXED COSTS              │                                   │
│                              │                                   │
│  1 Employer's requirements   │                                   │
│  2 Site staffing             │                                   │
│  3 Site accommodation        │                                   │
│  4 Attendant labour          │                                   │
│  5 Miscellaneous labour costs│                                   │
│  6 Facilities and services   │                                   │
│  7 Temporary works           │                                   │
│  8 Mechanical plant          │                                   │
│  9 Non-mechanical plant      │                                   │
│ 10 Sundry items              │                                   │
├──────────────────────────────┴───────────────────────────────────┤
│                            TOTAL                                  │
├──────────────────────────────────────────────────────────────────┤
│                        SUMMARY TOTALS                             │
└──────────────────────────────────────────────────────────────────┘
```

Figure 2.12a

```
CONTRACT:  5 Storey Office Block          TENDER REF:   90/53
CONTRACT PERIOD:  45 weeks
TENDER ALL-IN RATES  -  TRADESMAN:        LABOURER:
TENDER SUBMISSION DATE:  15 Oct. 1991
```

| 1 - EMPLOYER'S REQUIREMENTS |||||||
TIME-RELATED ITEMS	Description	No off	Floor area	Hire rate	No.of weeks	Total sum
Accommodation						
Architect	8mx4m mobile	1no	32 sm	40.0	45	1800
Engineer	5mx3m mobile	1no	15 sm	35.0	25	875
Clerk of Works	4mx3m mobile	1no	12 sm	30.0	30	900
Telephone						
Rental	Telephone + ext	1no		6.0	45	270
Calls	Provisional/wk			8.0	45	360
Testing/Samples						
Brickwork panels	2 sample panels			sum		300
Cubes	Concrete cubes	6no		5.0ea	18	540
Other items						
Computer	1512K computer	1no		25.0	30	750
Surveying equipment						
Level	GK 100 Eng	1no		30.0	30	900
Theodolite	Watts Microptic	1no		50.0	12	600
Chainman	Labour	8hrs/ week		6.0	20ave	960
				TOTAL		£8255

Figure 2.12b

```
CONTRACT:  5 Storey Office Block          TENDER REF:   90/53
CONTRACT PERIOD:  45 weeks
TENDER ALL-IN RATES  -  TRADESMAN:        LABOURER:
TENDER SUBMISSION DATE:  15 Oct. 1991
```

1 - EMPLOYER'S REQUIREMENTS

FIXED COST ITEMS	No.	Description	Labour	Plant	Mat.	Total
Accommodation						
Erection and dismantling	1no	8m x 4m	320	50	100	470
Fitting out/ decorating			270		130	400
Office equipment			120		400	520
Transport to and from site				150		150
Telephone						
Installation	1no	Tel. + extension			150	150
Removal fee					30	30
Other items						
Site notice board	1no	4m x 3m				
Erect			70			70
Supply					200	200
Dismantle			40			40
Computer stationery					150	150
Software					400	400
TOTAL			820	200	1560	2580

Figure 2.12c

54

Many of the larger-sized contracting organisations have developed their own preliminaries proformas.   In this way, the estimator becomes familiar with the pricing policy within the company.

At tender adjudication stage, no matter how realistically the preliminaries have been priced, they are always subject to management scrutiny.   Pencil sharpening exercises usually result in contract preliminaries being drastically reduced and the contract, if awarded, having to be run on a tight budget.

2.9.4 Check List of Preliminaries

The following is a 'check list' of the more important project overheads which feature in preliminaries.   Sums of monies must be built up for each according to the particular circumstances and duration of the proposed contract.

(1) Site Supervision

A detailed assessment of the staff to be engaged on the project. Cost per week is assessed including salary, expenses and car allowances.   A realistic assessment must be made of the number of weeks to be allowed for site engineers, production control staff and site clerks.   The total cost of each is to be multiplied by the number of weeks, to give the total site supervision allowance.

(2) Setting Out

On a large contract the allowance for setting out will be included in site supervision.   On the smaller contract assistance will be required for the site manager during the initial contract stages. The build-up must include for the cost of pegs, profiles, lines and the hire of surveying instruments.

(3) Travelling Time and Expenses

The 'All-in Rate' does not include for this item.   The travelling time must be allowed for all operatives travelling to the site in order to cover for non-productive time which may average out at about one hour per day per operative.   Refer to the National Working Rule Agreement for details of radius allowances.   The provision of transport for carrying labour to the contract must also be included.   This is however dependent on the location of the site, availability of service transport, and the firm's policy regarding the provision of transport for the operatives.

(4) Third Party Insurance

This may be included as part of the company's general third party cover for all contracts.   A separate quotation may however be obtained; an average allowance is 1.6% of the wage roll.

(5) Fire Insurance

Quotations to be obtained as the contractor is responsible for insuring the building against fire risk during construction. Average fire risk is 0.15% on the contract sum and 0.20% for all risk policy.

(6) Contract Bond

Premiums vary according to status of contractor. Quotations should be obtained. Figures range from 0.20 to 0.50% of the contract sum. A bond may be required to cover 10% of the contract sum and in certain cases this may fall directly on the company directors in the form of a personal guarantee.

(7) Welfare - Toilet Facilities

Cost of hiring portable latrine units plus cost of locating and connecting to sewer. A water supply to provide separate washing facilities is also required. The cost of attendance in cleaning out the toilets must also be allowed, a common allowance being one hour per day. On completion a dismantling cost and removal from site must also be allowed.

(8) Offices, Stores and Mess Facilities

Cost of transporting, erecting, fitting out, lighting, heating and hiring must be allowed. On completion of the project the cost of dismantling and transporting from site must be included. On a phased site an allowance must be made for further dismantling and re-erection during the project. Allowances to be made for office cleaning facilities on the larger project.

(9) Site Services

Allowances must be made for temporary water supplies to the offices and mess accommodation. Water supplies will also be required for mortar and concrete mixing points.

Electricity will be required for temporary lighting, offices and mess. The provision of a central power supply board will also need consideration.

Drainage connections will be required for site latrines.

Charges for water may be checked with the local water board. The average charge is 0.30% of the contract sum plus the cost of standpipes, hoses and barrels.

(10) Clerk of Works or Resident Engineer

Specific reference must be made to the requirements of the preliminaries. Allowances must be made for the hire of suitable accommodation adequately fitted out to suit the specification.

Allowances to be made for clearing out and providing mess facilities for the Clerk of Works and provision of refreshment at site meetings.

(11) Safety and Welfare

Cost to be considered include safety association fees if applicable, complying with safety requirements, first aid boxes, provision of protective clothing, tea-making, washing and drying facilities and the cleaning of offices and mess.

(12) Telephone

An assessment is required of the installation cost, rental and call charges during the contract period. A pay telephone can be installed for the use of subcontractors. A connection may also be required for the Clerk of Works.

(13) Temporary Works

Consideration must be given to temporary fencing for compounds and hoardings to the site boundary, the cost of forming temporary site access roads, road and footpath crossings. An allowance may also be made for damage to road kerbs and footpaths.

(14) Signboard

Allow for providing timber support and signboard. Size to be assessed. Quotation may be obtained for standard signboard.

(15) Cleaning Site on Completion

Cost to be assessed of cleaning out building after each trade during construction. A quotation may be obtained from an office cleaning firm for cleaning out the building on completion.

(16) Construction Plant

Reference must be made to the method statement or plant schedule for major items of plant not readily incorporated in the unit rates. An estimate of the requisite time on site should be made for each item of plant and multiplied by the appropriate hire rate. The cost of transporting and removing plant from site must be included. Sums must also be assessed for hardstandings for plant and the cost of laying crane tracks.

(17) Scaffolding

The area of external and internal scaffolding will require assessment from the layout drawings. Quotations for special scaffolds for demolition and protective screens may be obtained. Allowance must also be made for scaffold towers and special attendance items for subcontractors.

(18) Fixed Price Allowances

There is great uncertainty in these fields in respect of infla-
tionary fluctuations. Graphs of the more important material
prices should be kept, which can be projected forward to predict
the likely movement. Trade union wage agreements occurring
during the contract period must be allowed for.

(19) Sundry Items

Other matters include attendance of nominated subcontractors and
suppliers which may be allowed in the preliminaries or priced in
the prime cost sums. Allowances must be made for protection
against inclement weather and winter working. Defects liability
costs may be assessed from cost records from previous similar
contracts.

2.10 ADJUDICATION OF AN ESTIMATE

Adjudication is the action taken by management to convert an
estimate into a tender. The process involves a review of the
estimate by the contractor's senior management in order to ensure
that a realistic and competitive bid is submitted. Many of the
factors considered at the decision to tender stage should again
be reviewed in the light of an ever-changing construction market.

2.10.1 Completion of the Estimate

This involves preparing an analysis of the totalled bills of
quantities in order to indicate the extent of the contractor's
own work compared with that of the domestic and nominated subcontractors and suppliers. The extent of monies included for
provisional sums, dayworks and contingencies will also be indicated.

    Adjustments to the estimate can be made for late quotations
received from both material suppliers and subcontractors. A
summary of the monies included for the various items of preliminaries may also be prepared. At the tender adjudication stage
it is often far too late to start adjusting individual rates and
as a result, cuts are often made to the contract preliminaries
in order to produce a more competitive bid. Allowances will
also be necessary for firm price adjustments where a fixed price
tender is to be submitted.

2.10.2 Report to Management

A concise report should be presented to the management clearly
indicating the extent of the work. This should include

(1) A brief description of the project

(2) A statement of the methods of construction upon which the estimate is based

(3) Note of any major assumptions made in the preparation of the estimate

(4) Any need for qualification of the tender or for an explanatory letter to clearly indicate any assumptions made

(5) Any mark-up included on any subcontractor or supplier's quotation

(6) An assessment of the profitability of the project. Within the larger organisation standard estimating summary forms may be available. These enable the major sections of the estimate to be easily reviewed and adjustments made. A model Adjudication Report Form (E/ES/10) is indicated in the I.O.B. Code of Estimating Practice[1]

(7) The time for which the tender is to remain open for acceptance.

The data collected during the estimate must be available during the adjudication meeting for reference.

2.10.3 Adjudication of the Estimate

The adjudication process is the responsibility of management. During the adjudication, management should give consideration to the following

(1) Any items included in the report to management

(2) The conditions of contract - any risks inherent in the project and not adequately covered by the contract conditions

(3) Contractual risk - assessment of any fixed price contingency

(4) Review of the plant allocation within the preliminaries including any adjustment due to changes in the methods of construction

(5) Adjustment to the terms of quotations received from one's own subcontractors

(6) Effect of the capital requirements for the project on current work in progress and the cash requirements and borrowing levels during the project

(7) Final review of the allocation of monies to the contract preliminaries

(8)   Current work load and the effect of the new contract on site staffing and technical staff

(9)   Market conditions - availability of work, current interest rate on loan accounts

(10) Assessment of the percentage allowance for general overheads

(11) Addition of profit percentage.

The actual tender figure can now be determined.

2.10.4   Submission of Priced Bills

At the time of tender submission it is normal practice simply to return the form of tender in the special envelope provided.   The form of tender states the contractor's bid in monetary terms.

The priced bills of quantities will be called forward from the three lowest tenders for checking and analysis by the architect.

At this stage the contractor's management must decide how the difference between the total of the net rates shown in the draft bill and the agreed tender figure is to be shown.   Three methods of distributing the mark-up are indicated in Section 6.02 of the I.O.B. Code of Estimating Practice.[1]   Possible methods are

(1)   Increase the unit rates by an agreed percentage so that the whole difference is included in the measured rates.

The percentage adjustment may however be varied in the form of a tender loading in order to return higher profits on items of work to be carried out during the early stages of the contract. In this way the cash flow position can be substantially improved by the contractor.

The method has drawbacks also, as any reduction in the quantity of work will result in a larger profit reduction.

(2)   The unit rates are left net and the whole of the difference is included in the contract preliminaries.

In this way the contractor is sure of recovering all his overheads as the preliminaries are not subject to any adjustment at the final account stage.   This however tends to inflate the preliminaries value and any variations to contract, both additions and omissions, are undertaken at net rates.

(3)   The unit rates are left net and the whole difference is included as a percentage addition on the final summary page.

Any combination of (1), (2) or (3) may alternatively be used.

2.11 ANALYSIS OF TENDER PERFORMANCE AND BIDDING THEORY

2.11.1 Bidding Theory

The underlying assumption of bidding theory is that to each marginal change of mark up there is a corresponding change in the probability of success.   Neither the consistency and reliability of net cost estimating nor the data concerned with risk and return is adequate to justify the exercise of the theory in the United Kingdom construction market conditions.   Mannerings[4] and others[6,7,8,9] have reviewed tender success and, if the theory were to be adopted, we would expect the frequency of a bid at each percentage point removed from success to be somewhat as shown below.

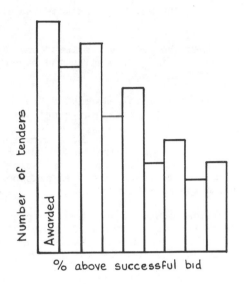

In fact only firms in which a director was closely concerned with tenders, with a restricted area of operation, and had a well defined marketing policy appeared to have statistics of this form. Others had a model peak some distance removed from success, suggesting that the special effort to gain tendering success was likely to involve some pencil sharpening rather than an adjustment of profit margin.

2.11.2 Success Rates in Construction Firms

What then, can be considered a satisfactory level of tendering success?   An analysis of three years' tendering performance within a building firm indicated the following results.

Year	Number of tenders submitted	Number of contracts awarded	Success Rate
1977	56	12	1 in 4.6
1978	44	10	1 in 4.4
1979	50	14	1 in 3.6

The average success rate over a three-year period is 1 in 4.2. This may be considered a satisfactory success rate when considering the construction climate over the time period.

2.11.3 Data to be Collected to Analyse Tender Performance

Few firms analyse their tendering performance but, should they do so, then experience might be gained of the application of bidding strategy based on the following data.

(1) The margin between the net cost estimate and the success-ful tender sume.

(2) The margin between the net cost estimate and the average ender sum (if available, as this eliminates the eccentric but successful bid as a factor).

(3) The unit cost or similar values relating to recent success-ful tenders by type of building and form of construction.

(4) The names of firms competing for the contract. These will normally be known competitors where the contractor tenders for work with local architects. Information relating to competi-tors may often be obtained from subcontractors or suppliers pro-viding quotations for competing contractors.

(5) The likely interest shown by the firms competing for the contract. This information may be obtained by undertaking a discreet marketing policy. The number of firms deciding to 'take a cover' will also provide an indication of the keenness of compet-itors.

(6) The range of tender results should be made available with-in four to eight weeks of the tender date. The architect will normally circulate tender results after analysis of the lowest bids and the decision to appoint a contractor. This procedure of circulating tender results should discourage contractors obtain-ing information via the 'grape vine' or the free flow of informa-tion between contractors after the bid has been submitted.

From the tender analysis report sheet in Figure 2.13, the following data may be obtained.

(a) The range of tender prices submitted.

(b) A percentage comparison of one's own submission against the successful bid and any other competitor's bid which may be of direct interest.

(c)   The range of margin allowed for profit, additional margins
levied against nominated subcontractors, suppliers and
domestic subcontractors' quotations.   These are possible
areas of adjustment which could have been undertaken at
the tender adjudication stage in order to provide a more
competitive bid.

(d)   A brief summary of the tender adjudication adjustments in
the form of additions or omissions.

2.11.4 Analysis of Tender Performance

The analysis of tender results leads one to critically reconsider
the company's whole tendering policy.   The following areas of
investigation may be considered.

What action must be taken to improve tendering performance?

(1) One solution may be, to be more selective regarding the
decision to tender.   This is mainly dependent upon there being
a readily available supply of enquiries on the market.   In times
of recession one may not be able to be selective in any way.

(2) Abortive tendering should be avoided as it only wastes
valuable estimating time;   in this context a number of firms
adopt a policy of 'covering' rather than disappoint the architect
responsible for sending out the enquiry.

(3) A comparison of tender results from the last range of
similar building projects may indicate that only a marginal adjustment is necessary in order to become more competitive.   Tender
adjudication meetings should take account of past tender performance on similar types of work in order to determine areas where
adjustments can be made.

(4) Some assessment of the probability of success on the one
hand and profit on the other, should thus be available to the
adjudicating committee.   If there is inconsistency in nett cost
estimating then the conclusions lose in reliability.   On the
other hand when reliable data is aggregated they may give substance
to probability assessments which accord with bidding theory.

Further data arising from achieved profit (or loss) compared,
for classes of construction, with expectation at the time of
adjudication, afford further information on the incidence of risk
and the probability of achieving the planned return.

For a more detailed discussion of competitive bidding see
Harris and McCaffer.[8]

Tender Analysis

Contract				Tender No.	
Job description				Address	
Architect		Quantity surveyor		Client	

Type of contract	with J.C.T. quantities	without J.C.T. quantities	CC 1	Negotiated	Date returned

Degree of competition

1	2	3	4	5	6	Total
						C cover

% comparison

Market conditions

Work load	
Materials	
% preliminaries	Profit margin
Adjudication adjustments	
Comments	
Position			Date	

figure 2.13

Tender Analysis							
Contract — Stanweld Holdings						Tender No.	81/30

Job description
Industrial factory development consisting of six units, access road and siteworks

Address
184 Buxton Rd
Stockport

Architect	Quantity surveyor	Client
D P & Associates Stockport	Sandy, Book & Partners Manchester	Stanweld Eng.

Type of Contract	J.C.T. with quantities	J.C.T. without quantities	C.C.I.	Negotiated	Date returned
	Drgs, bills and full drawings available	—	—	—	28/5/81

Degree of competition

1	2	3	4	5	6	Total
Snapes	S & V (our bid)	W. Thorley	H. Ball	Cole Bros.	B & W Const.	6
585520 –	592184 –	598200 –	610582 –	621400 –	633819 C	C cover

% comparison

—	1·14	2·16	4·28	6·12	8·24	

Market conditions

Work load	Keen to obtain work for the later end of year. Market conditions becoming difficult
Materials	Present rate 9% per annum – 0·75% per month

% preliminaries	9	Profit margin	5 %	N.S.C. attend.	5 %

Adjudication adjustments	Preliminaries reduced from 14% to 9%. Adjustments made to supervision/staffing and plant
Comments	Fixed price contract; net cost estimate including preliminaries approximately £548 000

Position	Second		Date	7/6/81

figure 2.13 (completed)

65

2.12   ANALYSIS OF TENDER PERFORMANCE - WORKED EXAMPLE

The following example indicates an approach to the analysis of
tendering performance based on research undertaken by Mannerings.[4]

2.12.1   Success Patterns Developed

The research was based on analysing the tender performance of
seventeen firms.   From the details of past bids three patterns
of success were developed.   Figure 2.14 indicates the A, B and C
distribution patterns from plotting the number of tenders submitted
against the percentage above the successful tender.

   The characteristics of the firms with the 'A' distribution were
as follows

(1)   Careful monitoring of the decision to tender with keenness
       and participation shown by the directors

(2)   Direct involvement of directors in the tender preparation
       and adjudication

(3)   Adjustment of profit margins in the light of market
       conditions

(4)   Medium-sized firms with a planned expansion programme
       within their own field of experience

(5)   Working radius confined to a defined area.

2.12.2   Analysis of Data Collected

Data was collected during 1979 for a medium-sized contractor.
During the period forty competitive bids were submitted of which
fourteen were successful.   This represented approximately fifty
per cent of the company's turnover, the remainder being obtained
by negotiation.

Tender No.	Our bid	Lowest bid	Difference	% Difference	Range
1	54987	54987	–	–	Awarded
2	21400	19700	1700	7.9	6-8
3	87400	84200	3200	3.66	2-4
4	54563	48765	5798	10.62	10-12
5	147290	142207	5083	3.45	2-4
6	11763	11763	–	–	Awarded
7	12300	12080	220	1.78	0-2
8	78483	78483	–	–	Awarded
9	12870	12870	–	–	Awarded
10	20903	21697	794	3.66	2-4
11	36617	34070	2547	6.95	6-8
12	33592	32522	1070	3.18	2-4
13	29895	29895	–	–	Awarded

Tender Success Patterns

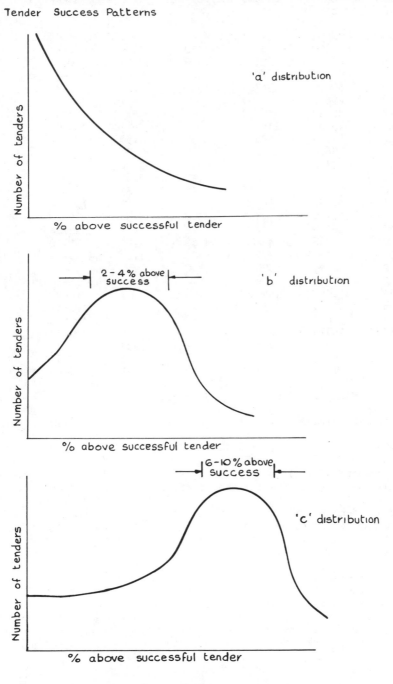

figure 2.14

Tender No.	Our bid	Lowest bid	Difference	% Difference	Range
14	37551	37551	–	–	Awarded
15	57200	54179	3030	5.29	4-6
16	69400	62400	7000	10.08	10-12
17	67501	67100	401	0.60	0-2
18	60800	58764	2036	3.34	2-4
19	29800	29800	–	–	Awarded
20	46928	46928	–	–	Awarded
21	213300	213300	–	–	Awarded
22	83255	82800	435	0.50	0-2
23	55600	49854	5746	10.30	10-12
24	51772	50948	925	1.78	0-2
25	116307	113210	3097	2.66	2-4
26	37168	36877	291	0.78	0-2
27	54300	54300	–	–	Awarded
28	127700	123400	4300	3.36	2-4
29	68200	68200	–	–	Awarded
30	51166	46400	4766	9.31	8-10
31	17425	17200	225	1.29	0-2
32	64000	59600	4400	6.87	6-8
33	27746	26930	816	2.90	2-4
34	162786	161000	1785	1.09	0-2
35	55700	55700	–	–	Awarded
36	21654	21654	–	–	Awarded
37	28973	28973	–	–	Awarded
38	17002	16400	602	3.54	2-4
39	73500	75100	1600	2.13	2-4
40	87400	91100	3700	4.23	4-6

2.12.3 Summary – Range of Tender Results

Range	Awarded	0-2	2-4	4-6	6-8	8-10	10-12
Number	14	7	10	2	3	1	3

The numbers of tenders have been plotted against the percentage range above the successful tender and shown in histogram form in Figure 2.15.   This indicates an 'A' distribution plotting.   It can be seen from the histogram that if the margin was adjusted by 2% a further seven contracts would have been won.   With an adjustment up to 4% seventeen additional contracts would have been awarded.

The tender success rate of 1 in 2.85 is considered above average and is due to the contractor mainly being selective at the decision to tender stage.   This factor closely relates to Mannerings' conclusions which indicated that firms with the greatest measure of tendering success were those which were more selective in their choice of contract.[4]

68

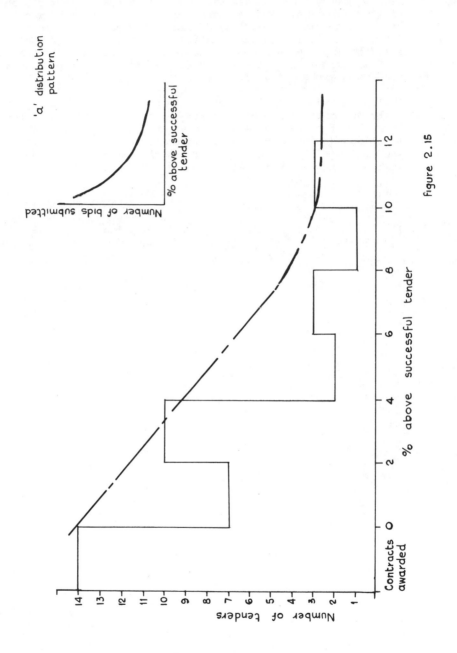

'a' distribution pattern

Number of bids submitted

% above successful tender

Figure 2.15

Number of tenders

% above successful tender

Contracts awarded

69

2.12.4 Bidding Theory and the Contractor

Bidding theory relates marginal change to a change in the probability of success. The existence of a relationship between the bid price and the probability of winning is an acceptable fact. A change of several per cent introduces a difference of success rate from say one in eight to one in five; thus a change of one-half per cent in a margin is unlikely to have much impact upon the actual probability of success.

The analysis of tender performance using the above method of analysis can aid contractors to improve their tendering performance. By knowing the percentage adjustment to be made, in order to improve the success rate, it is up to the directors to formulate the firm's policy in the light of the market conditions, current work load and the anticipated returns.

REFERENCES - PRE-TENDER PLANNING

1. The Institute of Building Code of Estimating Practice
   Fourth Edition, 1979

2. Institute of Building - Estimating Service Paper No.33,
   Summer 1979, The Administration of a Tender

3. Supplement to the Code of Estimating Practice, Information
   Required before Estimating

4. Mannerings, R., M.Sc. Thesis, University of Manchester
   Institute of Science and Technology, 1970, A Study of Factors
   Affecting Tendering Success in Building Works

5. Institute of Building - Estimating Service Paper No.19,
   Winter, 1975, Supplier's Invitation to Tender for the Supply
   of Materials

6. Fine, B. and Hackemen, G. - Estimating and Bidding Strategy
   Building Technology and Management, September 1970

7. Fine, B. - Tendering Strategy, Building, 25 October 1974

8. Pinn, J.C. - Competitive Tendering and Bidding Strategy
   National Builder, November 1974

9. Harris, F. and McCaffer, R. - Modern Construction Management
   (Crosby Lockwood Staples, London, 1977)

BIBLIOGRAPHY

Institute of Building Estimating Information Service Papers

No.2, October, 1971 - Pricing Preliminaries

No.3, January, 1972 - The Relationship between Estimating and
                      Work Study

No.4, April, 1972 - Materials Purchasing - The Link between
                    Estimator and Buyer

No.5, July, 1972 - The Estimating Team - Some Aspects of its Work

No.6, October, 1972 - Pricing Attendance on Nominated Sub-contractors

No.7, January, 1973 - Sub-contractors - Invitation to Tender and
                      Adjudication of Quotations

No.12, April, 1974 - Planning in Relation to Estimating

No.30, Autumn, 1978 - Work Study as an Aid to Estimating

No.31, Winter, 1978 - Estimating the Plant Element

No.34, Autumn, 1979 - Contractor Selection - A Guide to Good
         Practice

No.35, Winter, 1979 - Computer-aided Estimating

Crawshaw, D.T., Building Research Information Paper 27/79,
        Project Information at the Pre-construction Stage

3 PRE-CONTRACT PLANNING

The following selective topic areas on pre-contract planning follow the procedures undertaken prior to commencing a contract.

The main points discussed relate to the principal factors involved at each stage. Various proformas used by construction organisations are included in a simplified format.

The topic areas are

3.1 Pre-contract arrangements prior to commencing a project

3.2 A. Organisation structure for a project
B. Organisation structure for a city centre development

3.3 Site layout planning

3.4 Placing of orders for subcontractors and suppliers

3.5 Requirement schedules

3.6 The master programme

3.7 Budgetary control procedures

3.8 Cash flow analysis - calculation

3.1 PRE-CONTRACT ARRANGEMENTS PRIOR TO COMMENCING A PROJECT

3.1.1 Procedures to be Undertaken

Prior to commencing a contract, liaison will be necessary between the contractor, architect, statutory undertakings and local authority. Initial contact will have to be made with key material suppliers and own and nominated subcontractors (if known) together with plant hire firms likely to be participating in the early contract stages.

The time period allowed for undertaking pre-contract activities varies widely depending upon the complexity of the works and the client's urgency to commence work on the site. The time period for possession of the site is usually stated in the contract appendix or in the preliminaries section of the bill of quantities. On the smaller project a period of 5 to 10 days is often adequate, while the larger and more complex project will probably require some 4 to 6 weeks to organise and plan.

The stages involved prior to the contract commencing follow a similar pattern in both large and small organisations. Within the larger firm procedures tend to be of a more formal nature.

It is important that the prospective site manager becomes involved in the pre-contract planning as soon as possible after the award of the contract. It is often the policy within large firms to appoint the site manager up to 4 weeks prior to a contract's commencement. This allows time for the site manager to familiarise himself with the bills of quantities and contract drawings and to participate in the preparation of the master programme. The site manager at this stage will organise the setting up of the site including the preparation of the site layout plan. The short term programme for the initial period of the contract may also be prepared together with finalising construction methods and plant requirements.

Within the smaller organisation, where the site manager is not appointed until the commencement of the contract, the pre-contract procedures will be undertaken by the contracts manager.

The stages undertaken during the initial pre-contract period are

(1) The pre-contract planning meeting
(2) The registration of drawings
(3) Arrangements for commencing work.

3.1.2 The Pre-contract Planning Meeting

A meeting will be held to announce the award of the contract and to acquaint all concerned with the general background information. This will assist in developing close co-ordination between the estimating, surveying and contract management teams and in the development of a team spirit.

The chief estimator or a director will act as chairman for the meeting and he should be fully conversant with all decisions taken during the preparation of the tender. The meeting may be used by the company to pass over the tender documentation from the estimating to the contracts department.

The following personnel will normally attend the pre-contract planning meeting

Chief Estimator

Responsible for

(1) Acting as meeting chairman

(2) Handing over all tendering data to the respective personnel,
      e.g. Estimate summary and adjudication data
           Build-up of net bill rates
           Summary of subcontractors' and suppliers' quotations
           Method statements
           Preliminaries build-up

Contracts Manager

Responsible for

(1) Organising the commencement of work by the programmed date

(2) Appointment of site manager and/or arrangements for transfer of site management personnel

(3) Preparation or assistance in the preparation of the master programme in conjunction with the planning engineer and prospective site manager

(4) Finalising the statement of construction methods and schedule of plant and equipment requirements

(5) Preparation of the site layout plan

(6) Preparation of expenditure budgets for labour, plant and preliminaries

Buyer

Responsible for

(1) Finalising quotations with suppliers and subcontractors

(2) Preparing schedules including co-ordinating material requirements with the master programme

(3) Placing orders with material suppliers and own and nominated subcontractors. In certain organisations it may be considered a quantity surveying function to place subcontractors' orders

(4) Preparing schedules of key dates for the delivery of materials

Chief Quantity Surveyor

Responsible for

(1) Checking and arranging for the signing of the contract documents

(2) Appointment of surveying staff for the contract

(3) Preparation of the contract valuation forecast and cash flow assessment

(4) Distribution of copies of the bills of quantities

(5) Preparation of forms of contract for own and nominated subcontracts in conjunction with the buying department

Office Manager

Responsible for

(1) Preparation of master files for the contract

(2) Distribution of all letters in relation to the contract
    (general office to act as central clearing house for
    contract mail)

(3) Appointment of clerical staff for the contract to assist
    with the site administration

(4) Arrangement of insurances

(5) Serving of notices and payment of fees

(6) Arrangement for office stationery and safety packs to be
    despatched to site

Chief Planning Engineer

Responsible for

(1) Preparation of master programme for the contract.
    This will involve a review of the tender programme and
    current drawings available. Liaison with the contracts
    manager or site manager regarding the sequence of work,
    key dates and labour resourcing

(2) Appointment of staff for undertaking short term planning
    procedures on site

The above items indicate areas of responsibility allocated to
each of the company departments. Responsibility for planning
and cost control may however be undertaken by a production control
section, as is often the case within the large construction firms.

3.1.3 The Registration of Drawings

It is of importance to the contractor that records are kept of
the receipt of all contract information as at some later stage
contractual claims may arise. From the initial stage a drawing
register must be kept to record the issue date of drawings received
from the architect and other consultants.

Communication channels must be set up which ensure that all
drawings are sent to the contractor's head office for distribution
by the office manager. In this way a full set of up to date
drawings is permanently held for reference at head office.
Similar communication and distribution channels should also be
established for correspondence.

3.1.4 Arrangements for Commencing Work

Careful planning at this stage can result in monetary and time savings during the contract. Consideration should be given to the following items in order to ensure a smooth start to the contract.

(1) The Preparation of the Site Layout Plan

This enables the site manager to consider access problems, the siting of offices and site accommodation and the schedule of items as outlined in section 3.2. The preparation of an adequate site layout plan is an essential pre-requisite prior to commencing work on site. On the smaller project a diagrammatic presentation may not be essential but layout considerations should be discussed between the contracts manager and site manager.

(2) Temporary Site Services

Applications must be made for all temporary services requirements during the pre-contract period, e.g. water, electricity and telephone services. The site layout plan will assist in indicating the proposed location of service requirements. Permission will also be required for connections to the existing sewers for toilets unless these form connections to the new drainage work.

(3) Licences, Permits and Notices

Licences are required for hoardings, gantries over a public right of way and for the storage of petrol or explosives on site. Permits are required for road closures, part road closures, catering facilities on site and overtime working. Notifications have to be made to comply with the requirements of the Building Regulations at the commencement of work and the obligations of the Factories Act. Statutory notices have to be obtained for posting on site at the commencement of work, such as an abstract of the general provisions of the Factories Act. A standard documentation pack containing all the relevant notices to be displayed and safety propaganda can be issued from head office.

(4) Small Tools and Equipment Requirements

Many of the larger firms provide small tools and equipment from the head office stores at the commencement of a contract. A small tools requisition schedule is completed by the site manager for delivery to site during the early stages of the contract. This enables the head office to take advantage of bulk purchases on small tools.

A pre-contract check list covering essential items is used within certain of the larger organisations. This provides an important guide to new site management personnel.

The Institute of Building Code of Estimating Practice (Section 7) deals with the action with a successful tender. This briefly covers the check on contract documents, distribution of information, an assessment of cost information, visits to the site and the final reconciliation.

3.2 A. ORGANISATION STRUCTURE FOR A PROJECT

A medium-sized contractor is undertaking six contracts within a 20 km radius of head office. The individual contracts vary in value from £80000 to £220000. The building firm has been established some 80 years and is controlled by four directors, each having a direct responsibility for a facet of the business.

An organisation structure for controlling the projects is outlined. The responsibility of the contractor's senior management and the services to be provided by the head office are shown with the emphasis on the relationship between the site and the various managerial functions.

3.2.1 Organisational Structure of Firms

The organisational structures of medium and large contracting organisations reflect the variety of activities and forms of expertise which characterise them. Similar common principles are evident when comparing firms with a similar number of employees or annual turnover but differences are such that the structure tends to show a marked variation.

The organisational structure of the business stems from the policy developed by the principals or directors. As a firm expands the nature of the organisation structure undergoes changes in order to meet the demands of the business.

Additional staffing requirements and an increased labour force employed on the projects will necessitate the introduction of strict control procedures. As further expansion takes place more formal procedures are developed to aid control and shorten the communication channels.

3.2.2 Head Office Organisation - Senior Management Level

Figure 3.1 indicates the senior management structure above site manager level together with the area of responsibility allocated to each of the company directors. All major contracts are normally under the direct control of the contracts director and he is assisted by the contracts manager in the control of the contracts. Minor contracts up to a value of £20000 are the responsibility of a further director controlling a number of foremen each engaged on a contract.

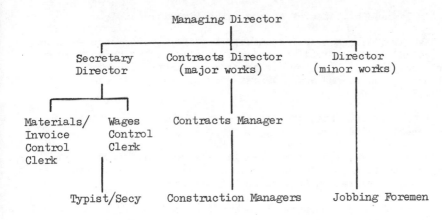

Figure 3.1

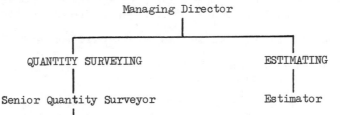

Figure 3.2

3.2.3 Responsibilities of the Managing Director

The managing director is responsible for the liaison between head office and the construction projects covering quantity surveying services, planning and various aspects of financial control. Estimating, surveying and planning services are under his direct control.

Figure 3.2 indicates the probable staff under the control of the managing director.

The quantity surveyors are usually all head office based and afford a service to sites as and when required, embracing re-measurement, valuation service and final accounts.

The managing director is the executive responsible to the Board for the day to day running and performance of the firm. Any list is likely to be incomplete as no list adequately shows the degree of delegation. The assumption here is that the managing director has a quantity surveying background.

Responsibilities of the managing director include

(1) Policy-making with the board of directors
(2) Appointment of staff
(3) Overall responsibility for quantity surveying and estimating procedures
(4) Financial control aspects - monthly cost/value comparisons
(5) Progress and cost reports - liaison with the contracts director
(6) Planning procedures at the pre-contract and contract planning stage
(7) Obtaining work - contact with clients
(8) Investment and raising capital

Turnover is currently in excess of £1.2 million and the policy of the company is to double turnover in the next three years. As expansion takes place, this may cause the managing director to relinquish responsibility for surveying and estimating procedures and the appointment of a surveying director.

3.2.4 Organisation Structure for Major Projects

Liaison with contract sites is obtained through the contracts manager who is responsible for co-ordinating materials, plant and labour between the contracts under his control. Weekly progress reports are prepared at site level and the contracts manager presents a monthly progress report to the contracts director.

Contract planning during the progress of the work is undertaken by the contracts manager in consultation with the construction manager. Short term planning procedures are the responsibility of the construction manager. Plant is largely hired by arrangement with the contracts director.

Figure 3.3 indicates the organisation structure for a factory project of £420000 value.

3.2 B. ORGANISATION STRUCTURE FOR A CITY CENTRE DEVELOPMENT

A multi-million pound city centre development is to be undertaken by a large contracting organisation. A suitable organisation structure for the project is outlined together with the responsibilities of the following site management personnel

(1) The project manager
(2) The site manager of a work section
(3) The contract quantity surveyor
(4) The site engineer

3.2.5 Job Titles in Relation to Head Office and Site Management Personnel

Various personnel in different sizes of construction firms are given a number of similar job titles, for example

Contracts Manager

A person responsible for organising a number of contracts at the same time. Each site will be controlled by a site manager. The contracts manager is generally head office based and visits all the sites under his control periodically. He normally works in a defined region or area and is responsible for the co-ordination of all contracts under his control.

Site Manager/Construction Manager

The person responsible on the site for controlling and organising the work. He is the representative of the main contractor. May be referred to as the construction manager or site agent in a civil engineering organisation.

General Foreman

The person in charge of the various site trades, responsible for co-ordinating all the trades. On the smaller contract the general foreman may act as the site manager if he is the representative of the contractor on site.

Project Manager

The title of project manager may be used for the person in charge of the larger type of project. He will be in control of a number of site managers employed on the various sections of the work, as in the case of a multi-million pound central redevelopment project divided into a number of phases all co-ordinated by the project manager. More usually, however, the title is reserved for a manager under whom a number of firms work together. On overseas contracts these may include design organisations.

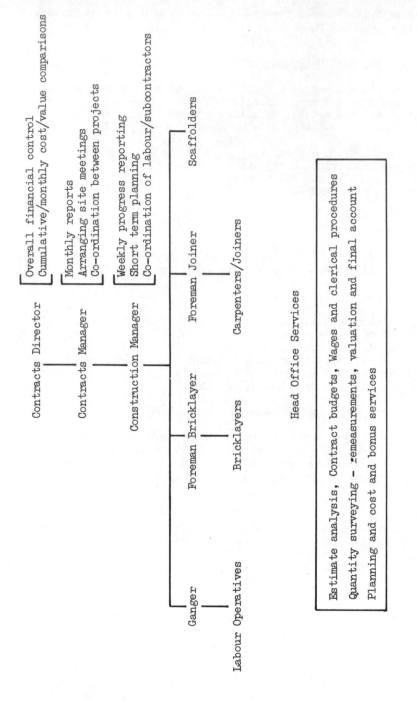

Contracts Director — Overall financial control / Cumulative/monthly cost/value comparisons

Contracts Manager — Monthly reports / Arranging site meetings / Co-ordination between projects

Construction Manager — Weekly progress reporting / Short term planning / Co-ordination of labour/subcontractors

Foreman Bricklayer — Bricklayers

Foreman Joiner — Carpenters/Joiners

Scaffolders

Ganger — Labour Operatives

Head Office Services

Estimate analysis, Contract budgets, Wages and clerical procedures
Quantity surveying — remeasurements, valuation and final account
Planning and cost and bonus services

Figure 3.3

82

Trades Foreman

   The person in charge of a particular trade, such as a foreman
joiner, bricklayer, steelfixer or plasterer.   The person in charge
of the labour gangs is termed a 'ganger'.   The trades foreman
receives daily instructions from the general foreman, or in the
case of a smaller contract, the site manager.

   The work is being undertaken by a large contracting organisation
with all services being provided on site (wages, quantity surveying
and cost and bonus facilities).

3.2.6 Head Office Management Relationship with Contract

A director in the head office will be given overall responsibility
for the contract.   This fact must be made clear to the client and
architect at the initial contract handover meeting.   This enables
the architect to have a direct link with the contractor's top management regarding any major problems during the contract.   All
senior management reports will be sent to the contracts director
and he will visit the site at regular intervals during the progress
of the works.

   Various alternatives at middle management level may be considered.
The contract may be controlled by a project manager under the direct
control of the contracts director.

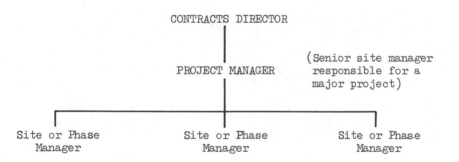

   As the contract will involve various phases or separate sections, each phase will be controlled by a site manager or site
agent responsible directly to the project manager.

   As an alternative the contract may be under the control of a
projects manager responsible to a contracts manager.   The contracts manager will be responsible for co-ordination between the
head office, site and architects.

CONTRACTS DIRECTOR

CONTRACTS MANAGER

PROJECT MANAGER

Site Manager (Phase 1)   Site Manager (Phase 2)   Site Manager (Phase 3)

Overlapping phases assumed.

3.2.7 Organisation Structure of the Project

It has been stated previously that all management services are to
be provided on site due to the size, nature and complexity of the
works.

The project manager is in control of the contract and all staff
engaged on the contract are accountable to him even though they
may be guided by head office in the carrying out of their duties.

A suitable organisational structure for the contract is illustrated in Figure 3.4. The organisational structure often separ-
ates the functions of cost and bonus, quantity surveying and
administration from the various trade functions. Plant, engineering and planning services are available from the central contract
organisation structure.

The main office area for the project will incorporate all
services for the individual phases. Centralised office accommodation will provide facilities for all site staff.

Site engineering services incorporate a team of engineers and
assistants responsible for all major setting out and the control
of line and level.

Centralised plant facilities will be provided to all phases
through a resident plant manager responsible for co-ordinating
plant requirements between the various site managers.

Figure 3.5 indicates an analysis of the staff based within
the centralised office on site.

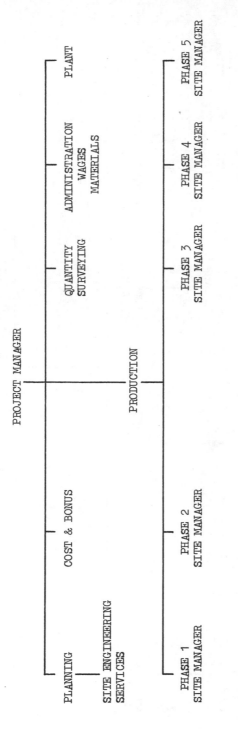

PROJECT MANAGER

PLANNING

SITE ENGINEERING
SERVICES

COST & BONUS

QUANTITY
SURVEYING

ADMINISTRATION
WAGES
MATERIALS

PLANT

PRODUCTION

PHASE 1
SITE MANAGER

PHASE 2
SITE MANAGER

PHASE 3
SITE MANAGER

PHASE 4
SITE MANAGER

PHASE 5
SITE MANAGER

Figure 3.4

85

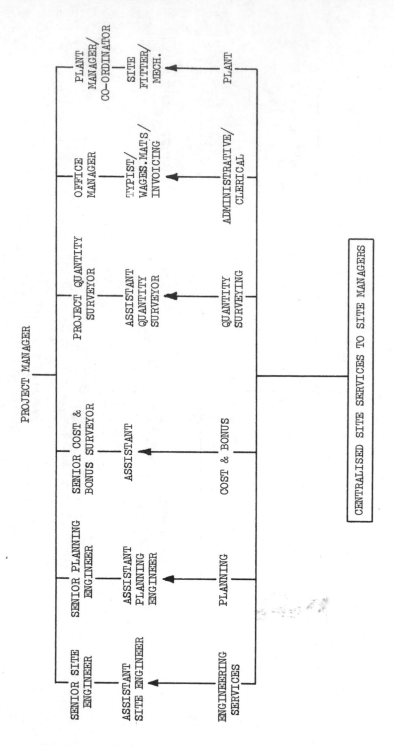

PROJECT MANAGER

SENIOR SITE ENGINEER — ASSISTANT SITE ENGINEER

SENIOR PLANNING ENGINEER — ASSISTANT PLANNING ENGINEER

SENIOR COST & BONUS SURVEYOR — ASSISTANT

PROJECT QUANTITY SURVEYOR — ASSISTANT QUANTITY SURVEYOR

OFFICE MANAGER — TYPIST/ WAGES.MATS/ INVOICING

PLANT MANAGER/ CO-ORDINATOR — SITE FITTER/ MECH.

ENGINEERING SERVICES

PLANNING

COST & BONUS

QUANTITY SURVEYING

ADMINISTRATIVE/ CLERICAL

PLANT

CENTRALISED SITE SERVICES TO SITE MANAGERS

Figure 3.5

86

3.2.8 Duties of Site Management Personnel Engaged on the Contract

The duties of the various site management personnel will be briefly outlined, together with an indication of their relationships with other members of the construction team with whom they have direct contact.

3.2.9 The Construction Manager/Site Manager

He is responsible for the overall control of the contract relating to all matters of site management.

Co-ordination will be required with the contractor's head office staff including the contracts manager, contracts director, company buyer and other related staff.

Daily responsibilities include

(1) Checking the progress position and taking the necessary action in the light of current resources

(2) Liaison with trades foreman

(3) Dealing with daily correspondence

(4) Keeping of a site diary

(5) Liaison with the clerk of works regarding standards of workmanship

(6) Taking instructions from the architect as and when necessary

(7) Co-ordination with subcontractors' representatives and subcontractors' foreman

(8) Checking the issue of information

Weekly responsibilities include

(1) Organising weekly planning meeting with site supervisors. Preparation of the weekly plan of work

(2) Co-ordination of subcontractors regarding the provision of adequate resources

(3) Assessment of plant utilisation and key material requirements

(4) Submission of weekly progress report to contracts manager

(5) Approval of bonus earnings and weekly cost returns

(6) Liaison with trades union representative

(7) Progress recording and maintenance of site records

(8) Ensuring that safety records and standards are maintained

(9) Maintaining adequate control of material wastage

(10) Liaison with head office personnel involved in the con-
     tract procedures.

Job descriptions in relation to the head of the contracts
department, contracts manager, site manager, senior surveyor,
general foreman, production surveyor, senior engineer, planner
and materials controller are outlined by R.A. Burgess and G. White
in Building Production and Project Management (Construction Press
1979).   In each case a general job description is indicated together with reference to qualifications, training and experience
requirements.

Many of the larger contracting firms issue job specifications
for various levels of head office and site management personnel.
This may take the form of a staff manual issued to cover the
activities of the company as a whole or individual departments.

3.3 SITE LAYOUT PLANNING

A multi-storey office block is to be constructed on a city centre
development project.

Outline factors to be considered when preparing a site layout
plan prior to commencing the contract are indicated.

Reference should be made to information available from the pre-
tender stage.   There will be the report of the site visit and the
items in preliminaries which directly affect site layout and
planning.

The following aspects should be considered.

3.3.1 Location of Offices and Site Accommodation

The contractor's site offices: These provide the information and
control centre of the site and must be placed so as to facilitate
the checking, supervision and security of the site.   As the perm-
anent structure is planned without the benefit of knowledge of
the specific requirement of construction method, the alternatives
available for siting offices may not be wholly satisfactory in
any case.   The design of office layout in relation to access,
materials storage, site handling and control can exercise a
considerable influence on the effectiveness of site management.

Fully fitted units of site accommodation are available which
can be established on site very quickly, and these can provide
flexibility and economy.   Much of the expense of temporary
accommodation is in re-establishing it, servicing, decorating and
furnishing on each occasion it is used.

Consideration may also be given to using existing buildings on the site prior to any demolition work.

Completed sections of the building may sometimes be used as site accommodation. For instance, hutting may be sited in the basement car park of a large complex.

Sectional timber buildings are usually held in the stores depot of companies and these may be made up to a certain size and layout to suit the needs of the particular site. The office complex should preferably be sited overlooking the site working area and access road. This enables site management to observe the daily movement of labour and plant together with all vehicles entering and leaving the site.

Separate toilet and mess facilities should be provided for the contractor's staff, client's representative and operatives.

The provision of car parking facilities will also need consideration - preferably located adjoining the site offices. This will need special consideration on a mid-city site and may involve providing specially fenced-off areas for the parking of vehicles visiting the site.

3.3.2 Location of Accommodation for the Clerk of Works and Resident Engineer

The contract preliminaries will indicate the extend of accommodation to be provided for the clerk of works, architect, resident engineer or client's representative.

A separate telephone service will be required, together with adequate mess facilities.

3.3.3 Location of Subcontractors' Accommodation, Site Stores and Canteen Accommodation for the Site Operatives

On a large project the subcontractors will normally provide their own site accommodation and stores. With a smaller project they may utilise the contractor's accommodation subject to the subcontract conditions.

An area on the site may be allocated for the location of all the subcontractors' accommodation and stores. On an open site a subcontractors' compound may be established.

The size and extent of the site canteen and mess facilities for the operatives is mainly dependent upon the extent and location of the works and the number of operatives to be employed on the contract. Large contracts located in remote areas may require provision for residence on site and full canteen and welfare facilities.

On most sites a secure compound is required and on sites of any consequence there is need for a site stores. A full-time storekeeper should be given responsibility for receiving, storing and issuing materials and equipment to the operatives.

A checker's office may be located at the site entrance. In addition to the immediate job of inspecting and checking deliveries, it is useful to have someone responsible to direct materials to that part of the site which is best able to accommodate them.

Areas of the site may be compounded off for secure storage of materials. Timber, reinforcement and other materials may be racked, selected and processed in the compound. On large housing projects a number of small compounds may be fenced off for the storage of goods adjacent to each work area.

Consideration may be given for the storage of material in parts of the completed building. For instance garages may be built early in the contract to provide lockable storage areas for the main contractor's and subcontractors' goods.

3.3.4 Location of Site Services

The site visit report will indicate the location and extent of temporary services to the site.

A temporary water connection will be required to supply the office accommodation, mess and subcontractors' requirements.

Standpipe locations will be required for the site mixing of concrete or for the mixing of mortar.

Supply mains must be protected against frost and traffic using the site.

Telephone facilities will be necessary for the site office and clerk of works or resident engineer. A pay telephone may be installed for the use of subcontractors.

Electrical supplies will be required for the contractor's office lighting, mess accommodation and stores. A power board may be located within the building area. A three-phase electrical supply may also be required for a tower crane.

Where a direct supply cannot be obtained from the local Electricity Board it may be necessary to introduce a mobile generator. Sometimes, in such circumstances, the client may have a supply and connections may be negotiated.

Consideration should be given to the provision of lighting on the site during the night. Theft and vandalism can be costly and the likelihood that people entering the site will be observed must deter such activities.

3.3.5 Temporary Roads, Hardstandings and Access to the Works

The provision of temporary roads for the movement of plant and materials is often a crucial matter.   The method statement prepared at tender stage will outline construction methods and plant items to be allocated to the contract.

On sites showing surface water problems the insertion of grip trenches or agricultural drains may assist in drying out the surface.

Roads or car park areas to be constructed on the site may be advanced in the programme so as to be available for use during the contract.   These may later be cleaned off and re-stoned to the correct levels during the later stages of the contract.

A high water table, marshy ground, soft clay or filled ground can introduce problems in the development of temporary roads. Failure can disrupt site progress and the variety of available forms of road structure is such that some solution is available in all but the most extreme cases.   The cost of scraping and maintaining the running surface can be a significant factor in choice.   Only on rare occasions is it necessary to introduce some form of rail or cable transport.

Hardstandings may be required for the location of plant or cranes undertaking lifting operations.   Pre-formed hardstandings consisting of stone or hardcore may be formed adjacent to roadways for the bulk storage of bricks, drainage goods or scaffolding, etc.

Where possible a one-way traffic system for vehicles entering the site should be adopted.   The site entrance and exit should be well signed.   Directory signs to the site may also be used.

3.3.6 Location of Plant

The location of major items of plant such as tower or mobile crane positions must be considered when preparing a layout plan. Radius load indicators may be shown in order that a crane coverage can be checked against load distribution.   Reference may be made to the crane manufacturer's data sheets for radius load indications. The best positions for plant may call for a re-assessment of material stockpiles, scaffold towers and waste chutes.

On civil engineering projects involving the use of large excavation plant the location of plant maintenance and fuelling areas needs to be considered.

Night storage areas will also be required for items of construction plant.   On the smaller contract the plant may be stored in a lockable compound overnight and at weekends.

Plant on the larger project can be stored in a defined area and immobilised during non-working hours.

3.3.7 Fencing, Hoardings and Protection of the Public

Preliminary clauses will indicate the extent of hoardings and fencing required to protect the public. Adequate protection of the public around the site perimeter may be achieved by the erection of protective fans, double boarded scaffolds to prevent dust, and the provision of adequate lighting adjacent to footpaths.

Lockable gates may be provided for site security purposes.

Site perimeter fencing may be constructed of

(1) Chain link fencing on metal, timber or concrete posts
(2) Timber sleepers set vertically in the ground with fabric mesh reinforcement fixed between
(3) Timber framing with plywood facing
(4) Timber framing clad with corrugated sheeting

Consideration must be given to personnel using an existing building; protected covered walkways should be provided to protect users and the public. Dust screens should be erected when breaking through into an existing building.

Public relations considerations: appearance, viewing areas and information boards should not be overlooked.

3.3.8 Material Storage Areas and Work Areas for Site Fabrication

Work areas on the site will be required for

(1) The fabrication of formwork
(2) The cutting, bending and fabrication of reinforcement
(3) The manufacture of small precast items such as lintels or spacer blocks for reinforcement

Storage areas on the site will be required for

(1) Bricks: pre-prepared storage areas will be required to receive palleted brick deliveries. Good access to the storage areas will be necessary for delivery vehicles.

(2) Timber: open timber racks may be constructed for different sections of timber. Undercover storage is required with thorough ventilation.

(3) Scaffold: racks may be used for the storage of scaffolding with metal storage drums for scaffold fittings

(4) Drainage goods: pipes and fittings can be delivered shrink wrapped or crated for storage on site. Drainage materials on a large site may be stored in small compound areas.

(5) Precast units: where possible deliveries should be phased
to suit the erection programme. Where units
have to be stored on site they should be stored
to avoid damage and double handling.

On restricted sites or congested city sites, phased deliveries
may assist in reducing site storage problems.

3.3.9 Other Items to be Considered

(1) Space around the building for scaffolding and the movement
of plant and materials.

(2) Material storage areas around hoists.

(3) Storage of inflammable materials such as oils, paints
and gas containers.

(4) Security and protection of electrical installation.

3.3.10 Site Layout Planning Examples

Figure 3.6 indicates the site layout plan for a four-storey reinforced concrete framed building. The offices and accommodation
have been located on the proposed car park area at the rear of
Short Street. Mobile cranes for the lifting of the precast
floor units are to be located in the street at the two positions
shown. The lifting of the floor units will be arranged for a
weekend period when the mobile cranes may be brought in for the
lifting operation. The handling of ready mixed concrete for
the floor beams and columns is to be by barrow and hoist as the
quantity required will only be relatively small.

Figure 3.7 shows the location of site accommodation on a
scaffold gantry situated over the pavement area. Above the
office roof level a fabrication area has been formed for the
manufacture and storage of formwork, reinforcement and general
materials. Refuse chutes, hoist and small pole hoist have been
located within the scaffolding together with a further storage
gantry at first floor level.

Figure 3.8 illustrates a site layout plan for a large city
centre development scheme to be constructed in six phases controlled from a site project office. The site is bounded on all
sides by busy city streets with a one-way traffic system running
through the centre of the re-development area. Part of the site
layout plan is illustrated.

3.4 PLACING OF ORDERS FOR SUBCONTRACTORS AND SUPPLIERS

The selection of subcontractors is an important factor to be
considered at the pre-contract planning stage. Reference will
have to be made to the quotations utilised in the estimate and

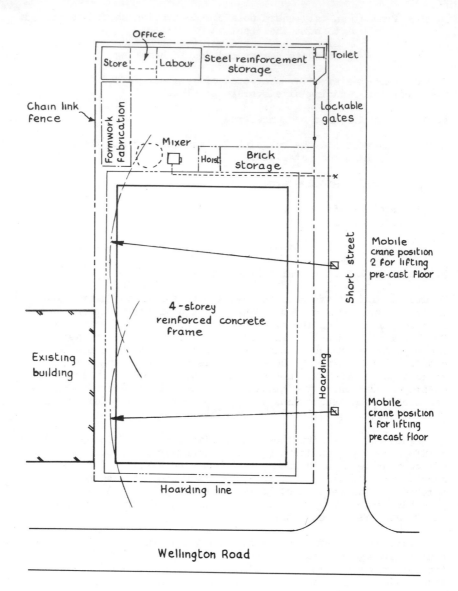

Office

Store | Labour | Steel reinforcement storage | Toilet

Chain link fence

Formwork Fabrication

Lockable gates

Mixer

Hoist | Brick storage

Mobile crane position 2 for lifting pre-cast floor

4-storey reinforced concrete frame

Short street

Existing building

Hoarding

Mobile crane position 1 for lifting precast floor

Hoarding line

Wellington Road

Site Layout Plan — 4-storey Reinforced Concrete Frame

figure 3.6

Site Layout Plan —
8 – storey Reinforced Concrete Frame

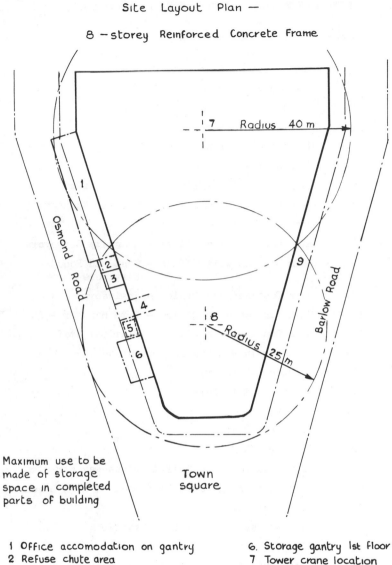

7 Radius 40 m

Osmond Road

Barlow Road

8 Radius 25 m

Maximum use to be
made of storage
space in completed
parts of building

Town
square

1 Office accomodation on gantry
2 Refuse chute area
3 Platform hoist and access
4 Unloading area
5 Small pole hoist located
  on scaffold

6. Storage gantry 1st floor
7 Tower crane location
8 Tower crane location
9 External scaffold and
  hoarding

figure 3.7

95

SITE LAYOUT PLAN - CITY CENTRE DEVELOPMENT

KEY: Reference   Description

Reference	Description
1.	Crane Slot - Crane 45 m Radius
2.	Crane Slot - Crane 40 m Radius
3.	Crane Slot - Crane 40 m Radius
4.	Crane Slot - Crane 50 m Radius
5.	Crane Slot - Crane 30 m Radius
6.	Main Stores
7.	Main Contractor's Administrative Office
8.	Main Contractor's Office - Project Manager
9.	Clerk of Works
10.	Main Contractor's Office - Quantity Surveyors
11.	Main Contractor's Office - Cost and Bonus Surveyors
12.	Main Contractor's Office - Engineers
13.	Main Contractor's Office - Site Manager - Phase I
14.	Main Contractor's Office - Clerical Staff
15.	Clocking-in Station for Operatives
16.	Testing Laboratory
17.	Canteen and Toilets
18.	Safety Office
19.	First Aid Post
20.	Checkers' Office
21.	Main Road for Town Traffic - one-way street
22.	Temporary Bridge over Main Road at High Level
23.	Site Hoarding
24.	Main Access Gate for Site Traffic
25.	Sign Board
26.	Entry/Exit for Operatives
27.	Site Toilets - Portaloo Units

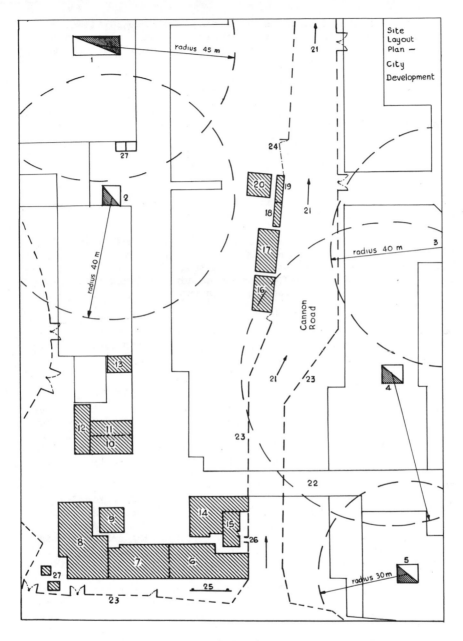

Figure 3.8

decisions made relating to the obtaining of any requotations or new enquiries. Subcontractors' requirements will also have to be co-ordinated with the master programme in order that a schedule of key subcontractors' dates can be prepared.

3.4.1 The Appointment of Subcontractors

The following points require consideration when selecting and appointing subcontractors

(1) The contractor's previous experience of working with the subcontractor and the latter's ability to organise and manage the subcontract work.

(2) The financial stability of the subcontractor, his payment terms and extent of claims consciousness.

(3) The subcontractor's ability to cope with the projected workload taking into account his current commitments. Certain main contractors have a policy of limiting the smaller subcontract firm to a maximum of three contracts at any one time. This is in order to prevent his labour requirements from becoming overstretched.

(4) The reliability of the subcontractor, standards of workmanship and his ability to co-ordinate with the contractor's site management.

3.4.2 Contracts with Subcontractors

It is important that the terms of the subcontract are fully understood by all parties. Written quotations adequately broken down to permit valuation should be obtained. Where possible the subcontractor's quotation should be related to the bill of quantities. In this way the extent of the contractor's margin can be readily established and key bill rates identified.

Wherever possible the subcontractor should be encouraged to sign a form of contract, e.g. the 'Blue' or 'Green' form of subcontract whichever is applicable. This ensures that payment terms and periods are clearly defined and that the subcontractor fully understands his obligation to the main contractor. A private form of subcontract may alternatively be used. In the case of the smaller firms, a letter accepting the subcontractor's quotation and stating the terms of the subcontract often provides an adequate agreement. The forms of subcontract can be prepared by the buying department or the contractor's surveyor responsible for valuation. As the quantity surveyors are to be dealing with subcontractors' accounts during the contract they are often in a better position to deal with subcontractors' contracts at the initial stage.

SUBCONTRACTOR'S QUESTIONNAIRE	DATE
CONTRACT	PLANNER
SUBCONTRACTOR	REF.

1. Time allocated on programme for completion of work

2. Sequence of work

3. Labour strength to be provided and number of gangs

4. Number of visits to be made to site

5. Information required prior to commencing work on site

6. Minimum notice required prior to commencement

7. Time required for approval of drawings

8. Date for main contractor to be furnished with the position of holes, pockets and chases

9. Date for taking of site dimensions

10. Information required from other subcontractors

11. Information required from the main contractor

12. Storage facilities required/or to be provided by subcontractor

13. Attendances

14. Delivery period for specialist material

15. Other relevant information

Figure 3.9

3.4.3 Subcontractor's Questionnaire

In order to assess the initial requirements of subcontractors and to provide them with contract information, a subcontractor's questionnaire may be utilised.   An example of the format utilised is indicated in Figure 3.9.

Refer to further notes relating to subcontractors in section 3.5 in relation to requirement schedules and co-ordination with the master programme.

3.5 REQUIREMENT SCHEDULES

At the pre-contract planning stage it is necessary to assess the contract requirements regarding

(1) The provision of labour resources
(2) Key material supplies
(3) The allocation of plant and equipment
(4) Key commencement dates for subcontractors and suppliers
(5) Information requirements from the architect or other consultant

In order to standardise procedures the data can be presented in programme format or on requirement schedules.   This enables key dates to be reviewed during the contract and information to be circulated to all parties concerned.

3.5.1 Schedule of Labour Requirements

The labour requirements for the contract may be indicated on the master programme in the form of a gang schedule, totalled and presented in histogram form.   This enables the actual labour engaged on the project to be matched with the planned labour force.   Alternatively the labour requirements can be shown on a separate labour schedule as in Figure 3.10.

3.5.2 Schedule of Material Requirements

This is normally prepared in conjunction with the buying department and planning engineer and allows the material requirements to be integrated into the contract programme.

It is essential that material requirements are checked from current drawings and matched against the totals in the bills of quantities.   The material schedule shown in Figure 3.11 indicates the key dates when materials are to be delivered to site.   The schedule may also indicate the supplier's telephone number, order number and actual delivery dates.   It is important that suppliers are kept informed of the contract's progress position with regard to any amendment to planned delivery dates.

To aid materials control the 'early warning system' may be introduced.   An example based on the principles of this system is outlined in Chapter 5.

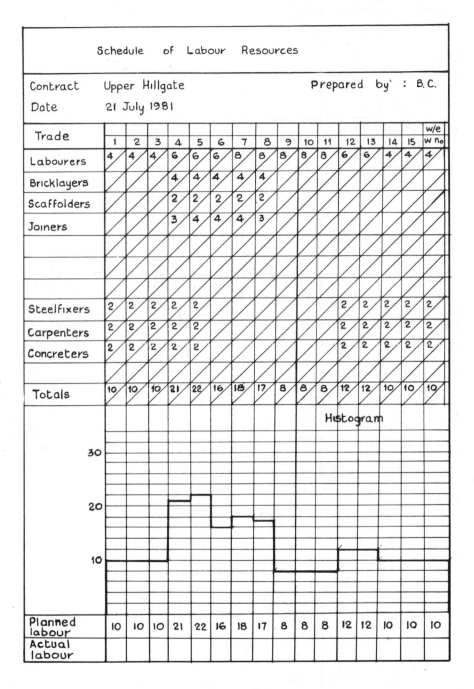

figure 3.10

MATERIALS SCHEDULE

CONTRACT

DATE

SHEET NO.

PREPARED BY:

Ref.	Material Description	Supplier	Address/ Tel.No.	Order No.	Quantity	Bill Ref.	Date Ordered	Key Dates			Remarks
								Notice Reqd.	Date Reqd.	Date Recd.	

Figure 3.11

3.5.3 Schedule of Plant and Equipment

The plant requirements for the project must be finalised after a review of the method statement and consideration of the plant allocated in the contract preliminaries. Methods of construction at this stage may be revised, provided they do not involve any additional expense and fall within the estimated cost.

Plant requirements must be phased in to suit the order and sequence of the master programme. A separate plant schedule may be indicated in bar chart form to show the key dates for the commencement and completion of major operations involving plant utilisation. Figure 3.12 illustrates a typical schedule.

The plant schedule enables the plant department to assess its resources relative to other contracts in progress. Arrangements must be made for plant to be hired from outside hire firms in the case of the company plant department being over-committed. The plant department must be kept informed of the site progress position, especially where this affects the movement of plant to and from the sites.

In order to assist in the initial setting up of the site a small tools and equipment check list may be used. An example of a suitable requisition for this purpose is indicated in Figure 3.13.

3.5.4 Subcontractors and Suppliers Schedule

The co-ordination of subcontractors and nominated suppliers into the contract planning is an essential requirement for the contractor. The schedule indicated in Figure 3.14 provides a summary of the major subcontractors and suppliers and highlights the notice required, bill reference and planned and actual commencement and completion dates.

The key subcontractors' commencement dates will also be indicated on the master programme. A separate subcontractor's programme may also be prepared in order to match related operations.

3.5.5 Information Requirements from the Architect and Other Consultants

The architect must ensure that full contract information is available to the contractor to meet the requirements of the master programme. The information requirement schedule in Figure 3.15 enables the contractor to request information from the architect in advance of the anticipated commencement date of an operation on site. This may be used for calling forward information of the following type

(1) Setting out drawings and the conformation of key dimensions
(2) Foundation details, bolt positions, pockets and holes for services

103

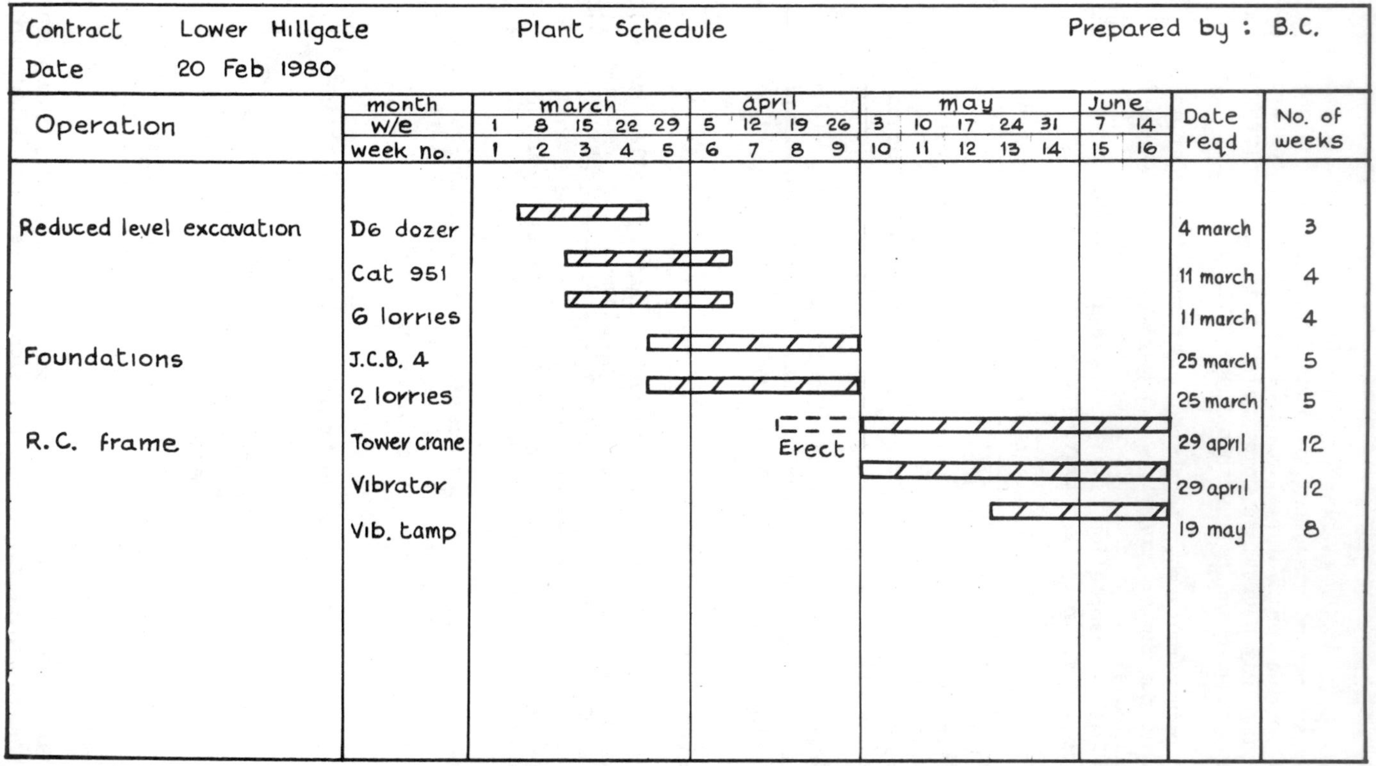

Contract : Lower Hillgate   Plant Schedule   Prepared by : B.C.

Date : 20 Feb 1980

Operation	month w/e week no.	Date reqd	No. of weeks
Reduced level excavation	D6 dozer	4 march	3
	Cat 951	11 march	4
	6 lorries	11 march	4
Foundations	J.C.B. 4	25 march	5
	2 lorries	25 march	5
R.C. frame	Tower crane	29 april	12
	Vibrator	29 april	12
	Vib. tamp	19 may	8

month: march — april — may — june
w/e: 1 8 15 22 29 | 5 12 19 26 | 3 10 17 24 31 | 7 14
week no.: 1 2 3 4 5 | 6 7 8 9 | 10 11 12 13 14 | 15 16

Erect (Tower crane)

figure 3.12

	CHECK LIST - SMALL TOOLS AND EQUIPMENT				
CONTRACT				1st LOAD REQUIRED	
DATE					

Quan.	Equipment	Del'y.	Quan.	Equipment	Del'y.
	Wheelbarrows			Safe	
	Shovels			Saw Bench	
	Picks			Sleepers	
	Brooms			Spirit Level	
	Buckets			Tapes	
	Chisels			Tarpaulins	
	Crow Bars			Thermometer	
	Tool Box			Waterproof Jackets	
	First Aid Equipment			Waterproof Trousers	
	Hammers - 3 kg				
	Lump Hammers			Power Drill - Dual Speed	
	String Line			Extension Lead	
	Setting Out Pegs			Grinders	
	Profile Boards			Temporary Light Set	
	Hose Pipe - 30 m lengths			Floodlights	
	tand Pipe			Traffic Light Equipment	
	Connectors			Safety Barriers	
	Ladders				
	Road Lamps			Canteen Tables	
	Temporary Barriers			Forms	
	Ranging Rods			Chairs	
	Notice Board			Office Desk	
	Rubber Boots			Water Boiler	

Figure 3.13

CONTRACT

DATE

SUBCONTRACTORS AND SUPPLIERS SCHEDULE

PREPARED BY

Ref.	Nomination/ Nominated Supply	Subcontractor	Address Tel.No.	Bill Ref.	Order No.	Notice Reqd.	Estimated			Actual		Date Called to Site
							Start	Finish	Period	Start	Finish	

Figure 3.14

CONTRACT

DATE

INFORMATION REQUIREMENTS SCHEDULE

ARCHITECT

Ref.	Information Required	From:	Bill Ref.	Anticipated Commencement Date	Information Required by	Date Information Received	Date of Request	Remarks

Figure 3.15

	P.C. AND PROVISIONAL SUMS –	CONTRACT	
	RELEASE OF INFORMATION	DATE	
ARCHITECT		TELEPHONE	
Bill Ref.	Information Required	Latest Date by which Order must be placed	Date Order placed
Builders' Work Information			

Figure 3.16

(3) Details of steel reinforcement bending schedules from the consulting engineer
(4) Colour, decoration and finishing schedules
(5) Services layout drawings
(6) Latest dates for nominations

Figure 3.16 enables the contractor to request information relating to nominations, provisional sums and builders' work detail. The recording of the dates of the release of information may later prove invaluable to the contractor for the build-up of claims for an extension of the contract period.

3.6   THE MASTER PROGRAMME

The master programme for the contract is prepared prior to the commencement of operations on site. It should be developed from the programme prepared at the pre-tender stage.

The programme will be prepared by the head office planning department in consultation with the contracts manager and site manager if appointed. It is important that the site manager participates in the planning procedures as he will later be responsible for interpreting the programme into a series of short term programmes. The site manager will be more likely to accept the master programme and develop it into a workable proposition if he has participated in its preparation.

Full information must be made available by the architect in the form of arrangement drawings (plans and sections) indicating sufficient detail to enable the sequence of operations to be determined. Nominations for suppliers and subcontractors should be available in order that their work may be integrated into the programme.

3.6.1   Presentation of the Programme

The master programme is normally prepared in bar chart form for contracts up to £150000 in value. On the more complex jobs over this value, network analysis techniques may be utilised. The advantages and disadvantages of the various planning techniques available to the contractor are outlined in section 4.1.

Bar charts are the most commonly used format for presenting the master programme within the medium-sized organisations. The master programme will indicate the following information

(1) The major phases of the work set out in the sequence of the site operations

(2) The contract commencement and completion dates

(3) Any annual or public holiday periods occurring during the project.

109

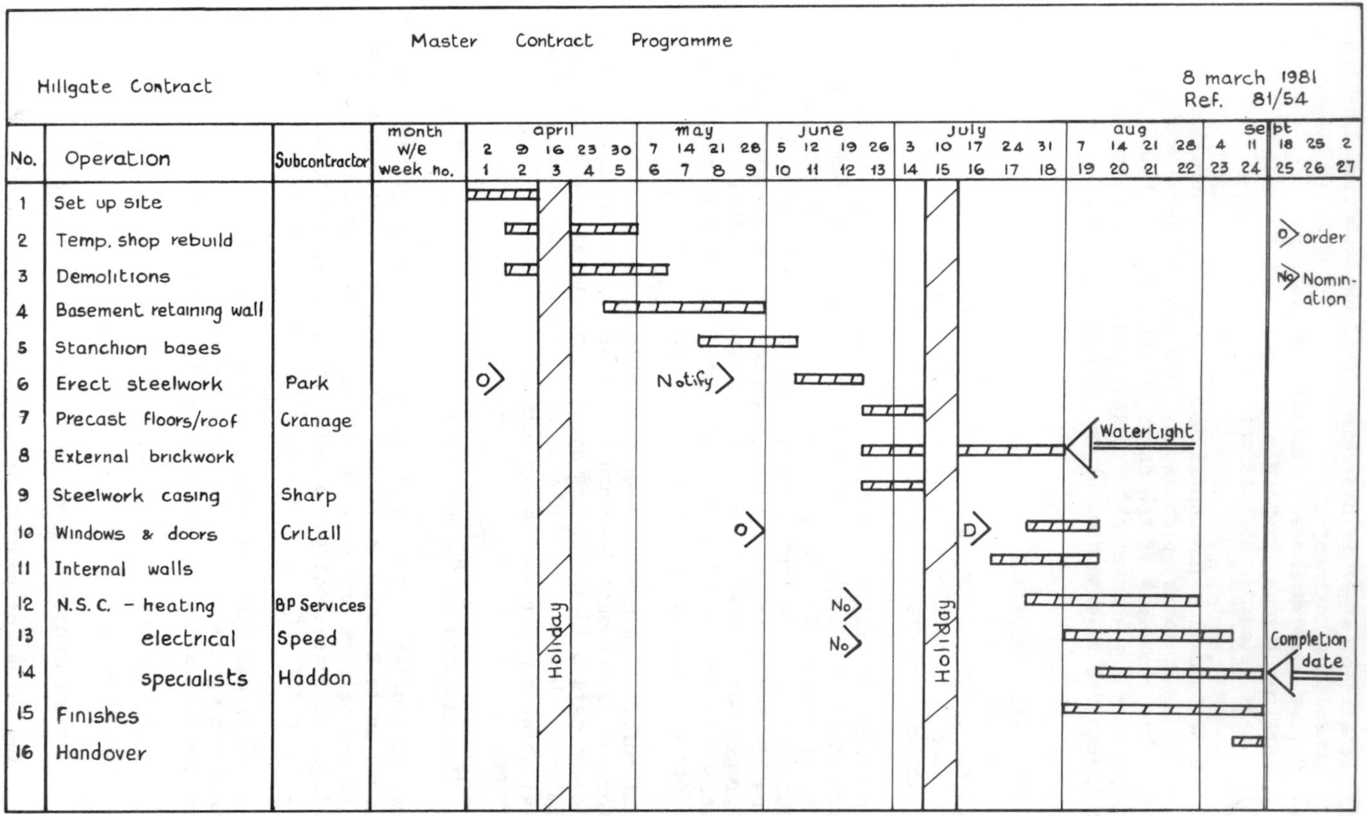
Master Contract Programme
Hillgate Contract
8 march 1981
Ref. 81/54
No.
Operation
Subcontractor
month
w/e
week no.
april 2 9 16 23 30
may 7 14 21 28
june 5 12 19 26
july 3 10 17 24 31
aug 7 14 21 28
sept 4 11 18 25 2
1 2 3 4 5 6 7 8 9 10 11 12 13 14 15 16 17 18 19 20 21 22 23 24 25 26 27
1 Set up site
2 Temp. shop rebuild
3 Demolitions
4 Basement retaining wall
5 Stanchion bases
6 Erect steelwork Park
7 Precast floors/roof Cranage
8 External brickwork
9 Steelwork casing Sharp
10 Windows & doors Critall
11 Internal walls
12 N.S.C. - heating BP Services
13 electrical Speed
14 specialists Haddon
15 Finishes
16 Handover
Holiday
Holiday
Notify
Watertight
Completion date
O
D
No
O order
No Nomin-ation

Figure 3.17

(4) Key dates relating to the completion or commencement of major stages of the work, e.g. roof watertight, completion of external service connections and handover date.

(5) Symbols to indicate key dates in relation to the commencement of subcontractors on site.

The programme chart may contain information relating to subcontractors' commencement dates and the latest dates when information is required from the architect. A variety of symbols may be introduced to aid control. An extract from a master programme is illustrated in Figure 3.17.

The master programme may also indicate planned labour and plant requirements. Copies of the master programme will be first submitted to the architect for approval in principle. This enables the architect to assess the validity of the contractor's programme regarding proposed dates for nominated subcontractors' work and key material supplies. A copy of the programme may be sent to the nominated subcontractors and suppliers in order to inform them of the anticipated commencement date of their own work.

3.6.2 Updating the Programme

An important part of the planning process is the updating of the programme as work progresses on site. Subcontractors and suppliers must be kept informed of any change in the progress position which directly affects key dates.

The responsibility for progress recording may be delegated to the site planning engineer, production control staff or simply be another task for the site manager.

Head office must be kept informed of the progress position on site. This may be achieved by the utilisation of a 'shuttle programme'. This involves sending a marked-up copy of the programme to head office each week. The progress position is entered onto the head office programme and the 'shuttle programme' returned to the site.

Refer to examples of the various formats of presenting bar charts, networks and precedence diagrams in Chapter 4.

3.7 BUDGETARY CONTROL PROCEDURES

The purpose of budgetary control is outlined together with the budgets which may be prepared prior to the commencement of a contract.

3.7.1 Budgets

A budget is a forecast or plan against which to monitor performance. In this context a contract programme may be termed a form

111

of budget against which the contractor matches progress during the contract. Control is exercised during the contract by prompt investigation into reasons for any variation from the budget or plan. Judgement is exercised to regulate performance in the execution of the plan. Within acceptable limits of deviation nothing further is required, but if deviation passes beyond these limits, action is necessary.

Without a plan or budget against which to monitor performance, one has no control.

Within a construction company budgets may be prepared for

(1) A forecast of the yearly turnover
(2) Cash flow forecasting
(3) Sales budget
(4) Estimating workload budget

3.7.2 Contract Budgets Prepared Prior to the Commencement of a Contract

As part of the pre-contract planning the preparation of budgets of forecast expenditure/cost, valuations, income and other measurable aspects of production permits contract performance to be monitored and controlled.

During the pre-contract period the following budgets may be prepared.

(1) Cumulative value/time budget from which forecast valuations may be obtained.

(2) Cost/time budget - against which performance during the contract may be monitored.

(3) Income/time budget from which cash flow forecasting may be prepared for a project.

(4) Preliminaries expenditure budget against which actual preliminaries expended may be matched.

(5) Plant expenditure budget based on the contract preliminaries against which actual weekly and cumulative plant costs may be monitored.

(6) Forecast labour expenditure budget expressed in man hours or pounds value. Actual labour expenditure can be matched with the budget relative to the overall contract position or relative to an individual operation.

The budget prepared for the cumulative value may be assessed from the contract master programme or may be based on an empirical assessment based on an S curve.

112

Examples of the various budget formats are illustrated.   It
should be noted, however, that their production is initiated by
a statement of policy as laid down by the Board.   The company
decides by reference to its risks and overheads where the emphasis
is to be placed in recording and reporting site activity.   Some
aspects of control can be handled on site and reviewed by a visiting manager.   Others are dependent upon the back-up services
available from head office (production control) which can only
function if it gains information on related progress and performance.   When production control personnel are engaged they would
be responsible for updating the budgets and producing the data to
match performance with budget.

3.7.3 Budget Presentation

Contract budgets may be presented in graphical or tabular form.
The budget prepared is compared at weekly or monthly time intervals with the actual performance achieved.   This enables vari-
ances to be assessed and management investigation and action
implemented where adverse trends are evident.   Graphical presentation highlights the relationship between budget and actual performance.

The following budgets are presented

Figure 3.18 - Illustrates a valuation forecast based on an
empirical assessment using the quarter/third approximation of
value and time.   Cumulative and monthly valuations are abstracted
and presented in tabular form.

Figure 3.19 - Illustrates a contract programme presented in
bar chart format with estimated budget values allocated to each
operation on a proportional time basis.   The weekly and cumulative
budget is summarised together with the forecast valuation dates.

Figure 3.20 - The information from the budget has been presented
graphically in the form of a value/time curve.   This enables the
actual value released and actual cost to be matched with the budget
during the progress of the work.

Figure 3.21 - This indicates the contract position at the end
of month 3.   The time and value variance may be observed together
with an analysis of the cumulative profit release.

Figure 3.22 - A forecast of the project cash-flow may be determined from an assessment of the cumulative income from valuations
and the projected cumulative cost.   This can be presented graphically by plotting the forecast value, cost and revenue from
valuations.   Net and gross cash requirements can be assessed for
each month end during the contract.   Based on this analysis,
arrangements can be made to provide finance for the contract.

Figure 3.23 - Illustrates the cash-flow diagram for the project
indicating the maximum gross cash requirements and the date at
which the contract becomes self-financing.

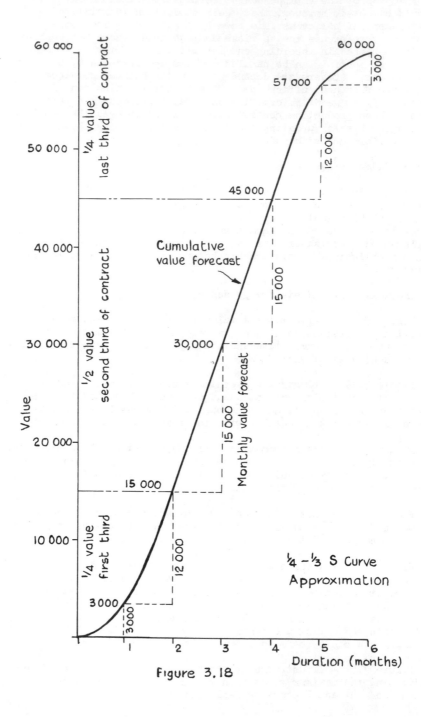

Figure 3.18

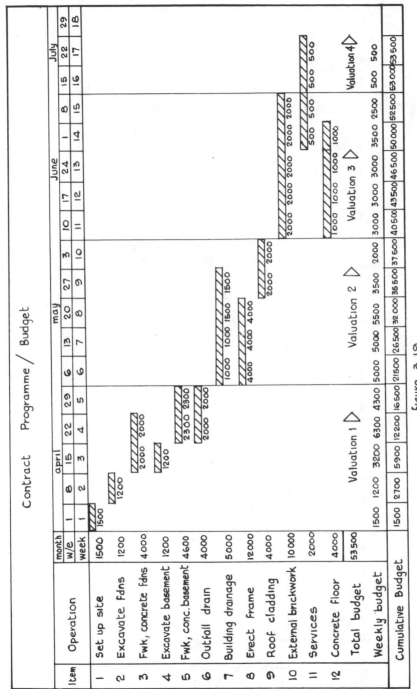

Contract Programme / Budget

Figure 3.19

115

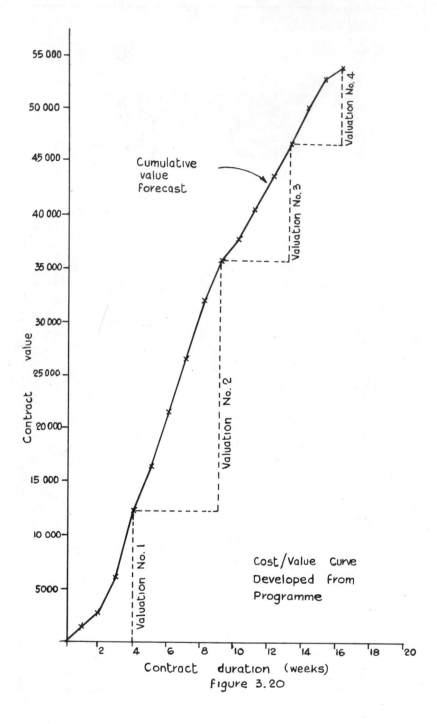

55 000

50 000

45 000

Cumulative
value
Forecast

40 000

Contract value

35 000

30 000

25 000

20 000

15 000

10 000

5000

Valuation No. 1

Valuation No. 2

Valuation No. 3

Valuation No. 4

Cost/Value Curve
Developed from
Programme

2   4   6   8   10   12   14   16   18   20

Contract   duration   (weeks)
figure 3.20

116

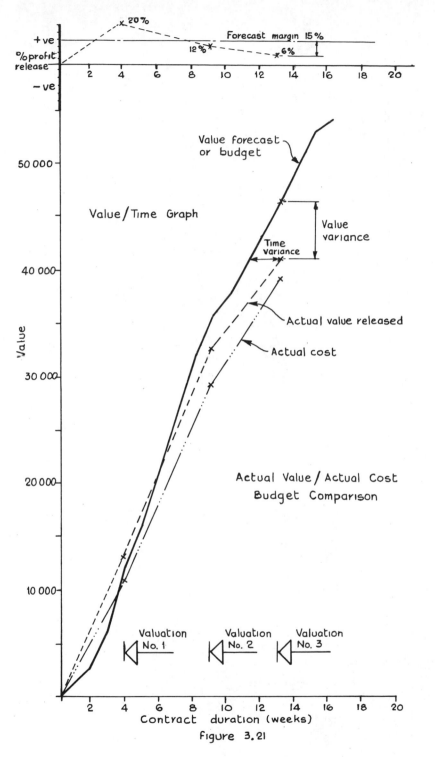

Figure 3.21

117

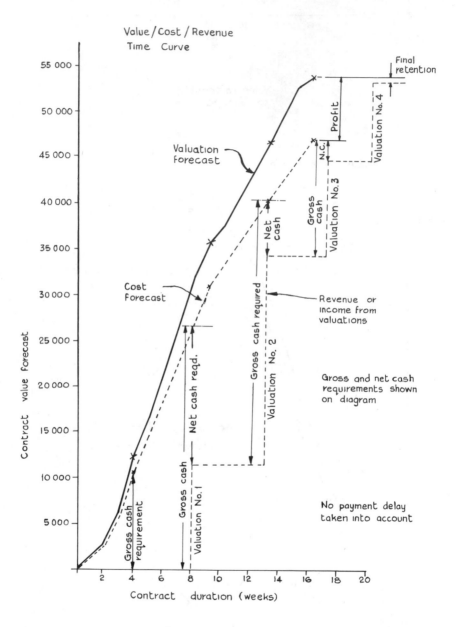

Figure 3.22

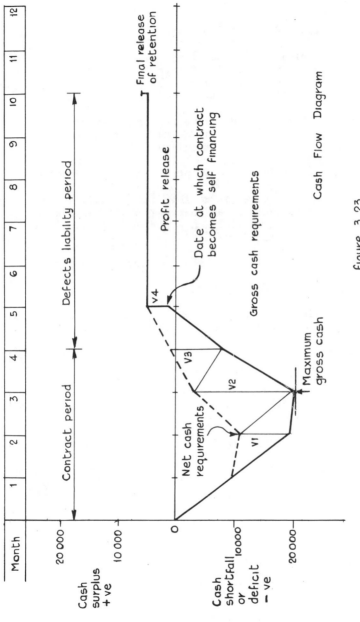

Figure 3.23   Cash Flow Diagram

3.8 CASH FLOW ANALYSIS - CALCULATION

A contract budget has been prepared and the monthly valuation forecasts are indicated.

Month	1	2	3	4	5	6
Monthly value (£)	8000	10000	12000	14000	10000	6000

The profit included in the estimate is 12% and payments are to be made monthly, payable within 28 days. Retention retained is to be 3% during the contract reduced to $1\frac{1}{2}$% at the contract completion. The defects liability period is to be 6 months.

An assessment is required of the cash requirements to be provided by the contractor. It may be assumed that the average delay in meeting the cost commitment is 4 weeks.

3.8.1 Information Required to Prepare a Cash Flow Forecast

(1) The contract budget in monthly or cumulative form. This may be based on an analysis of the contract programme or alternatively an empirical approximation (the quarter/third rule).

(2) The contract period, payment periods and retention details.

(3) The defects liability period.

(4) The anticipated profit release - rate of profit return per month dependent upon the tender loading.

(5) Delay in meeting the cost commitment for labour, material, plant and subcontractors' accounts.

(6) Analysis of the tender to indicate the percentage value of labour, materials, plant, subcontractors and overheads for each stage of the work.

3.8.2 Procedure in Preparing the Cash Flow Assessment

The data may be presented in tabular or graphical form in order to derive the net and gross cash requirements. The graphical presentation illustrates more clearly the whole relationship between value, cost, income and time. The delay in meeting the cost commitment can also be shown on the graph. The process of determining the cash flow requirements are as follows

(1) From the monthly and cumulative value forecast, calculate the cumulative cost based on the assumed profit release. The cumulative cost at each month end is given by

$$\text{Cumulative Value} \times \frac{100}{100 + \text{profit}} = \text{Cumulative Cost}$$

(2) From the cumulative value the forecast income from valuations may be determined. This equates from the cumulative value forecast minus the retention minus previous payments. The net monthly income may also be determined.

(3) Consideration must be taken of the delay in meeting the cost commitments. For this purpose the weighted average delay may be calculated. For example, if the following delays occur

Labour	– payment delay – 1 week
Materials	– payment delay – 8 weeks
Plant	– payment delay – 8 weeks
Subcontractors	– payment delay – 4 weeks

Analysis of cost relevant to each of the above assessed from the analysis of the estimate

Labour	– 20%
Materials	– 20%
Plant	– 20%
Subcontractors	– 40%

Weighted average delay in meeting the cost

Labour	= 1 x 20%	= 0.20
Materials	= 8 x 20%	= 1.60
Plant	= 8 x 20%	= 1.60
Subcontractors	= 4 x 40%	= 1.60
		5.00 weeks

For the purpose of the example 4 weeks has been assumed. The cost commitment period may thus be moved over 5 weeks from the end of the month in which the costs were raised.

(4) The cash requirement may be expressed in net or gross form.

Net cash required – Cumulative cost minus the cumulative income after the receipt of each monthly payment.

Gross cash required – Cumulative cost minus the cumulative income prior to the receiving of the monthly payment. This is the same sum as the net cash calculated above plus the monthly income just received.

The data is indicated graphically on the value/time curve in Figure 3.24 and in direct tabular form in Figure 3.25.

The cash flow diagram showing net and gross cash requirements is shown in Figure 3.26.

121

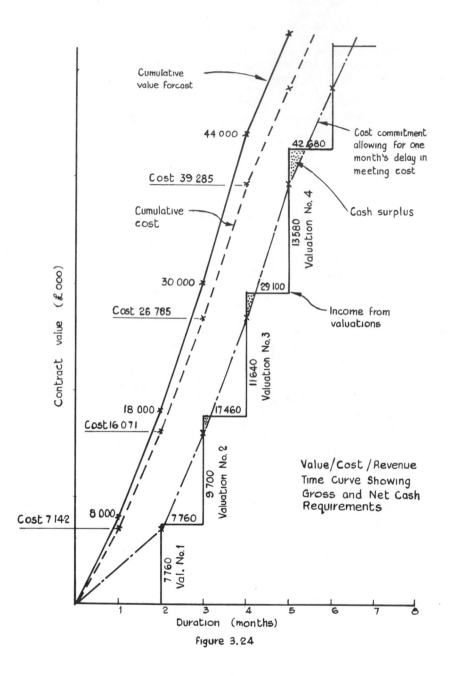

Figure 3.24

Value/Cost/Revenue Time Curve Showing Gross and Net Cash Requirements

3.8.3 Calculation of Net and Gross Cash Requirements

Month	Monthly Value	Cumulative Value	Cumulative Cost Value x $\dfrac{100}{100 + \text{profit}}$
1	8000	8000	7142
2	10000	18000	16071
3	12000	30000	26785
4	14000	44000	39285
5	10000	54000	48214
6	6000	60000	53571

Income from valuations

Month 1	Amount Due	8000	
	Less – Retention 3%	240	
			7760
	Less – Previous Payments		–
	Amount Due Valuation No.1		£7760

Month 2	Cumulative Value	18000	
	Less – Retention 3%	540	
			17460
	Less – Previous Payments		7760
	Amount Due Valuation No.2		£9700

Month 3	Cumulative Value	30000	
	Less – Retention 3%	900	
			29100
	Less – Previous Payments		17460
	Amount Due Valuation No.3		£11640

Month 4	Cumulative Value	44000	
	Less – Retention 3%	1320	
			42680
	Less – Previous Payments		29100
	Amount Due Valuation No.4		£13580

Month 5	Cumulative Value	54000	
	Less – Retention 3%	1620	
			52380
	Less – Previous Payments		42680
	Amount Due Valuation No.5		£9700

Month 6	Cumulative Value	60000	
	Less – Retention $1\frac{1}{2}$%	900	
			59100
	Less – Previous Payments		52380
	Amount Due Valuation No.6		£6720

Assessment of Net and Gross Cash Requirements

CASH FLOW REQUIREMENTS

MONTH	1	2	3	4	5	6	7
Cumulative Value	8000	18000	30000	44000	54000	60000	–
Cumulative Income	–	7760	17460	29100	42680	52380	59100
Cumulative Cost	3500	7142	16071	26785	39285	48214	53571
Net Cash Requirements	-3500	+628	+1389	+2315	+3405	+4166	+5529
Gross Cash Requirements	-3500	-7142	-8311	-9325	-10185	-5534	-1191

Gross cash requirements = Cumulative cost – income received to end of previous month

Figure 3.25

Month	1	2	3	4	5	6	7
Net cash	-3500	+618	+1389	+2315	+3395	+4166	+5527
Gross cash	-3500	-7142	-8311	-9325	-10185	-5534	-1191

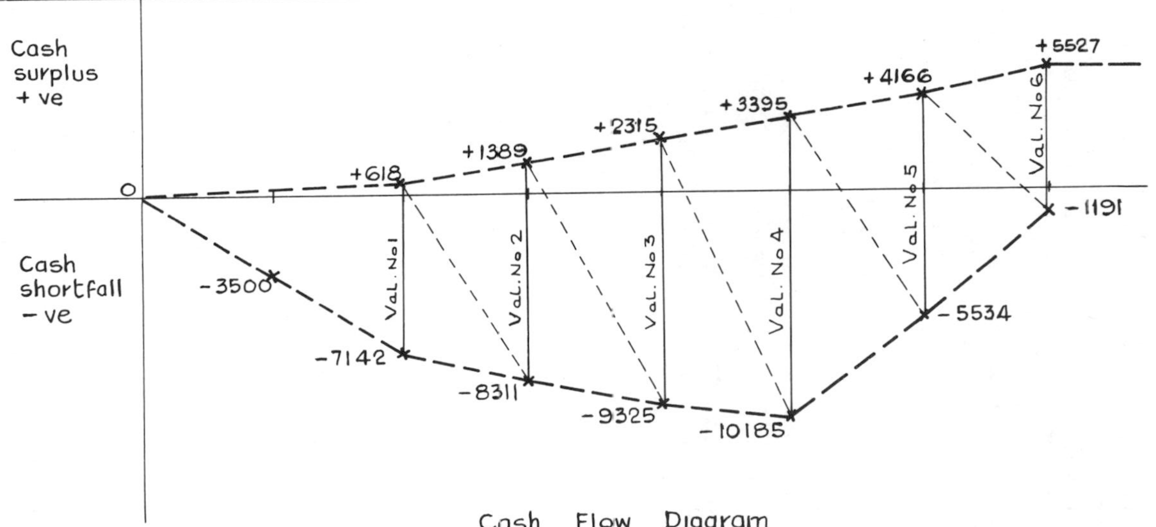

Cash Flow Diagram

Figure 3.26

125

3.8.4 Considerations for Improving the Cash Flow

The way a contractor can ensure that a contract will become self-financing is to delay paying out monies until the monthly payment certificate has been certified and paid. This is a great idea in principle but it just does not work in practice. Subcontractors and suppliers also have cash flow problems and will not allow the contractor sufficient credit facility without detriment to their own business. The following steps may be taken by the contractor to improve his cash flow position

(1) Ensure that valuations are submitted at regular intervals and certified by the architect within the specified seven-day period.

(2) The contractor should implement strict credit control procedures in order to follow-up certificates due for payment.

(3) Valuations or interim certificates should be accurate and represent the true value of work undertaken. Care should be taken in their preparation to ensure that they contain

(a) An assessment of the value of variations
(b) An accurate assessment of materials on site
(c) Provisional allowances for day-workers
(d) Increased cost to the date of its valuation

A pre-requisite to getting paid is to do a good job of work and ensure the contract is on programme.

(4) Sections of work subject to remeasurement should be measured and agreed during the contract period, preferably as soon as possible after the section of work has been completed. The remeasured sum may then be included in the interim certificates.

(5) The final account should be agreed within the specified period. This is normally within the defects liability period. The settlement of final accounts should not be allowed to drift on for years after the contract has finished as time erodes facts.

(6) Claims likely to result in a monetary gain should be carefully negotiated with the various parties and steps taken to settle these as part of the final account.

(7) The completion of maintenance defects should not be delayed beyond the liability period. This will ensure prompt issue of the final completion certificate, submission of the final account and the release of outstanding retentions. A regular check should be made on retentions due and action implemented by senior management to release retentions from old contracts.

(8) The credit afforded by suppliers and subcontractors must be assessed and full advantage taken of these facilities.   An average delayed payment of four weeks will improve the cash flow position by approximately thirty percent.

(9) Tender loading or the re-allocation of the profit element amongst the trade operations to be undertaken early in the contract period will marginally improve the cash flow position.

BIBLIOGRAPHY - PRE-CONTRACT PLANNING

Institute of Building - Site Management Information Service Papers

No.6, April, 1965 - Site Investigation and Preliminary Site Works

No.11, July, 1966 - Preliminary Procedures when Commencing a
                    Contract

Cooke, B. and Jepson, W.B., Cost and Financial Control for
    Construction Firms (Macmillan, 1979)

4 CONTRACT PLANNING TECHNIQUES

The following topics on contract planning cover various planning techniques. These include bar charts, critical path analysis, line of balance techniques and precedence diagrams.

Various examples from practice have been used relating to programming and sequence studies. Systems of planning used in industry have been adapted to suit the areas selected. Main points relating to the principal factors have been considered at each stage.

Topic areas included are

4.1 Planning Techniques Available to the Contractor

4.2 Programme Sequence for a Housing Contract

4.3 Programme Sequence for the Erection of Twenty-Four Reinforced Concrete Columns

4.4 Short Term Programme for a Laboratory Block

4.5 Network Programme for a Bridge Project

4.6 Network Analysis - Lead and Lag Terminology

4.7 Network Analysis - Crash Cost Application

4.8 Precedence Diagrams - Terminology and Relationships

4.9 Precedence Networks - Case Study

4.1 PLANNING TECHNIQUES AVAILABLE TO THE CONTRACTOR

A variety of planning techniques are available to the contractor. Three of these techniques are to be outlined indicating the advantages and disadvantages of each and the most suitable application in practice.

4.1.1 Planning Techniques Available

(1) Gantt or bar charts
(2) Line of balance charts
(3) Critical path techniques or network analysis
(4) Precedence diagrams

The utilisation and adoption of a planning technique within a company is dependent upon many factors. These include the policy of the board towards supporting a planning policy for use throughout the company to ensure that it is adopted at all levels of management. The planning expertise engaged, and the type and range of projects undertaken will also affect the range of techniques utilised.

4.1.2 Gantt or Bar Charts - Format of Presentation

Figure 4.1 illustrates a bar chart for a factory project showing progress recorded to the end of week 7. Bar lines represent the time period allocated to each operation and the relationship between the commencement and completion of each can be readily observed. Key symbols can be introduced on the bar chart to aid materials control and to show key dates in relation to nominated and own subcontractors. Figure 4.2 indicates the application of bar charts to a sequence of repetitive operations as may be applied to short term planning. Labour and plant requirements may also be indicated on the programme to aid resource levelling.

4.1.3 Advantages of Bar Charts

(1) Simple format.

(2) Readily understood at all levels of management.

(3) Lends itself to updating without total redrafting.

(4) Can show the relationship of planned to actual performance by marking up as the job progresses.

(5) The relationship between a master programme and any pre-tender and subsidiary programmes is readily seen.

(6) The chart may be used to indicate the demand for resources over each week or month by entering values and summing under the appropriate date.

(7) Requirements and key date symbols may be introduced to aid materials control.

(8) The format enables delays to be shown in the course of the work.

4.1.4 Disadvantages

(1) Complex, inter-related operations cannot be identified.

(2) There is no special emphasis on critical activities in working up such a chart directly.

4.1.5 Application

As a readily understandable statement of general interest bar charts may be applied to pre-tender, master programmes and short term planning procedures. At site management level detailed sequence studies can be presented in bar chart form showing alternative labour and plant resources.

Subcontractors' programmes may also be shown in bar chart format so as to relate them to those of the main contractor and other subcontractors with relative ease. It can provide all levels of

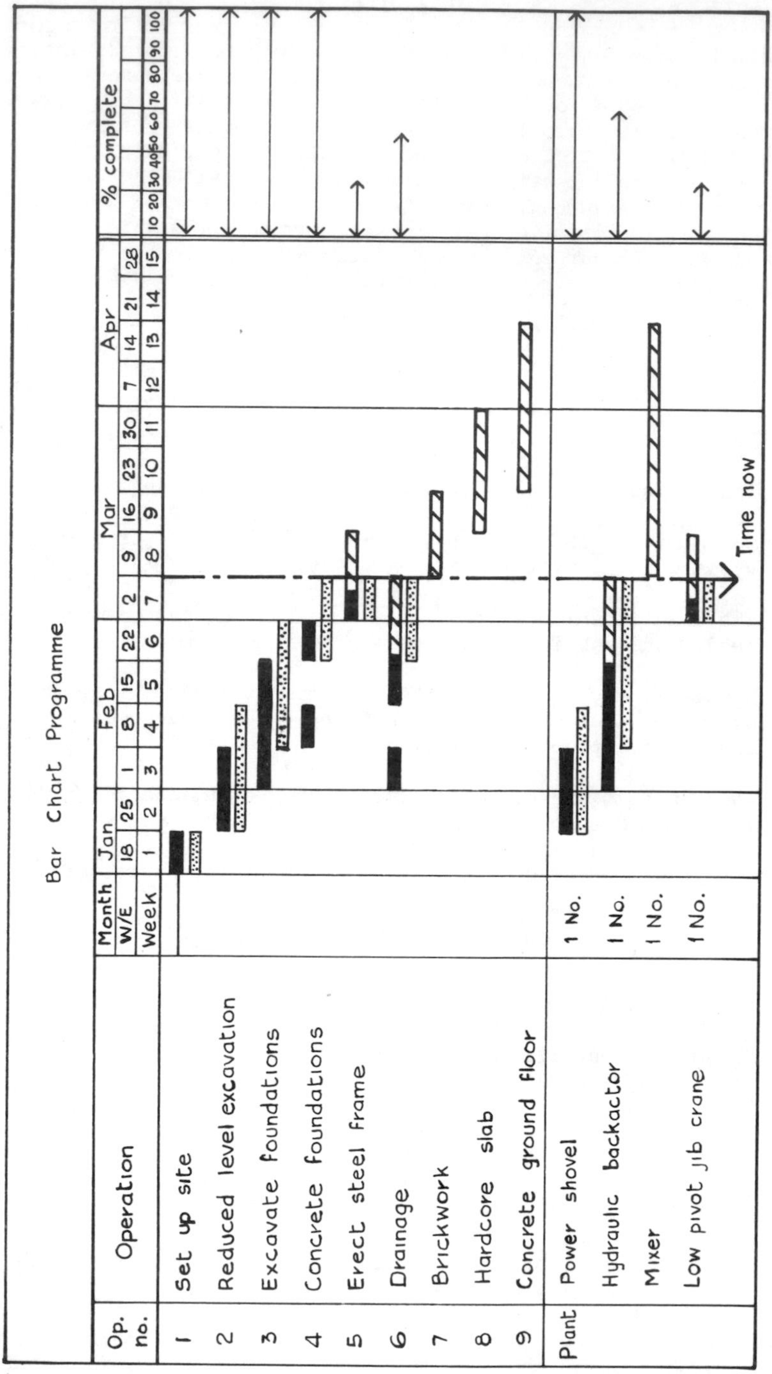

Bar Chart Programme
Op. no.
Operation
Month
W/E
Week
Jan
Feb
Mar
Apr
18 25 1 8 15 22 2 9 16 23 30 7 14 21 28
1 2 3 4 5 6 7 8 9 10 11 12 13 14 15
% complete
10 20 30 40 50 60 70 80 90 100
1 Set up site
2 Reduced level excavation
3 Excavate foundations
4 Concrete foundations
5 Erect steel frame
6 Drainage
7 Brickwork
8 Hardcore slab
9 Concrete ground floor
Plant
Power shovel 1 No.
Hydraulic backactor 1 No.
Mixer 1 No.
Low pivot jib crane 1 No.
Time now

figure 4.1

Column Sequence — Short Term Planning Schedule

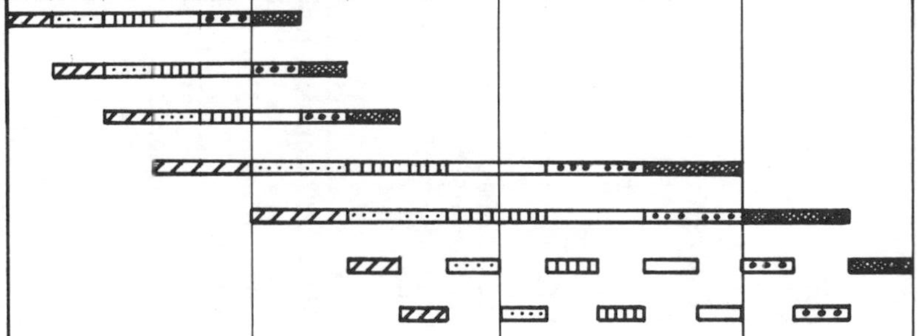

Op. no.	Operation	Duration	Labour	W1 m	t	w	t	f	W2 m	t	w	t	f	W3 m	t	w	t	f	W4 m	t	w
1	Excavate bases	1 day																			
2	Reinforcement	1 day																			
3	Concrete bases	1 day																			
4	Column reinforcement	2 days																			
5	Formwork – Fixing	2 days																			
6	Concrete columns	1 day																			
7	Formwork – strike	1 day																			
	Labour schedule																				
	Excavation gang	1 lab.		1	1	1	1	1	1												
	Steelfixers	2 No.			2	2	4	4	4	2	2	2	2	2	2	2	2	2			
	Concrete gang	3 No.				3	3	3	3	1	6		3		3	3	3		3		3
	Carpenters gang 1	4 No.							4	4	4	4	4	4	4	4	4	4	4	4	4
	Carpenters gang 2	4 No.								4	4	4	4	4	4	4	4	4	4	4	
	Total labour			1	3	6	8	8	12	11	16	10	13	10	13	13	13	10	11	8	7

Figure 4.2

131

management with a visual statement of the contract's progress. Like all graphical techniques it can be readily confused by excessive detail and complexity.

The bar chart lends itself to short term programming by reference to a master chart in a way which is less easy with other techniques.

It is imprecise in its observations of relative progress as the proportion completed at any date is not open to quantitative comparison.   If the proportion completed is guessed, then an optimistic guess can mislead.

4.1.6 Line of Balance – Format of Presentation

Figures 4.3, 4.4 and 4.5 indicate the format of presentation for three operations during the construction of ten houses.   Time buffers have been introduced between the completion of one operation and the commencement of the next.

Line of balance schedules are a series of inclined bar lines, one for each trade or operation.   The difference between line of balance schedules and a traditional bar chart is that the balance lines are inclined at different slopes to denote the rate of working of the various trades or operations.

4.1.7 Advantages of Line of Balance Techniques

(1) Vividly displays the rate of working of one trade against another.

(2) Relates the requirement of specified resources to the achievement of a planned completion date.

(3) Embraces the optimum deployment of resources when these are in different gangs on different repetitive tasks but all contributing to an output.

(4) Out of sequence working between related trades and unbalanced manning are eliminated by the exercise of the technique in establishing output targets.

(5) Schedules may be prepared from the chart as an aid to progressing materials deliveries.

(6) The schedule clearly indicates the number of units to be completed by a specific date.

(7) The principles of the planning system are readily understood at site management level.   The schedule is easily updated.   Actual performance can be compared with the planned requirements at any date.

(8) Regular progress recording highlights the need for increased gang requirements in order to enable the recovery of any lost time.

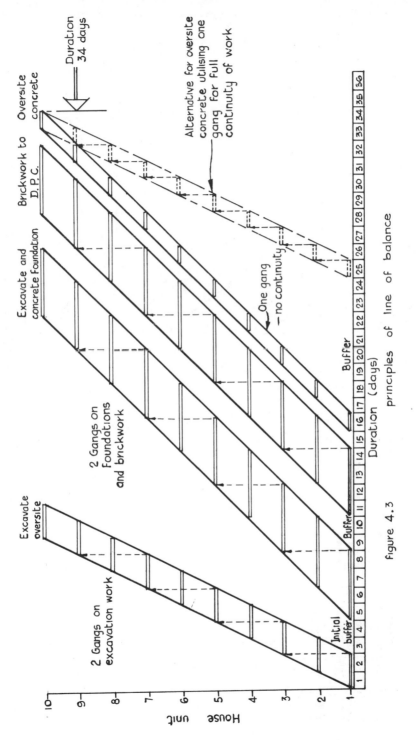

figure 4.3 principles of line of balance

133

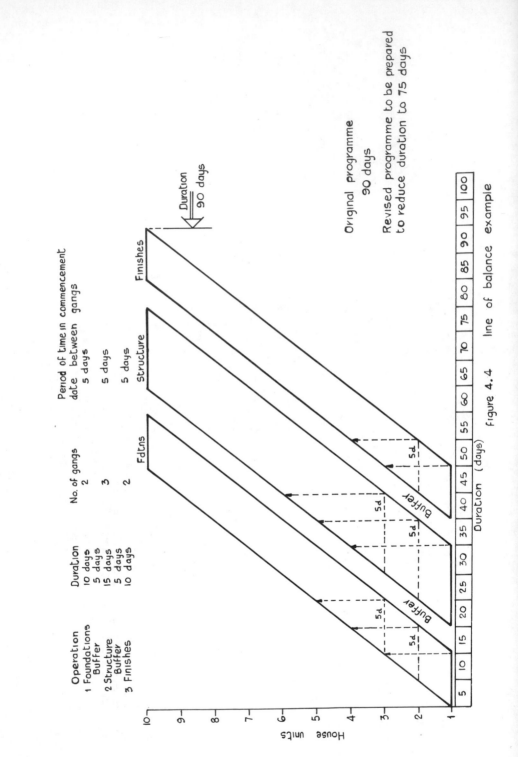

Operation	Duration	No. of gangs	Period of time in commencement date between gangs
1 Foundations	10 days	2	5 days
Buffer	5 days		
2 Structure	15 days	3	5 days
Buffer	5 days		
3 Finishes	10 days	2	5 days

Duration 90 days

Original programme 90 days

Revised programme to be prepared to reduce duration to 75 days

Figure 4.4   line of balance example

134

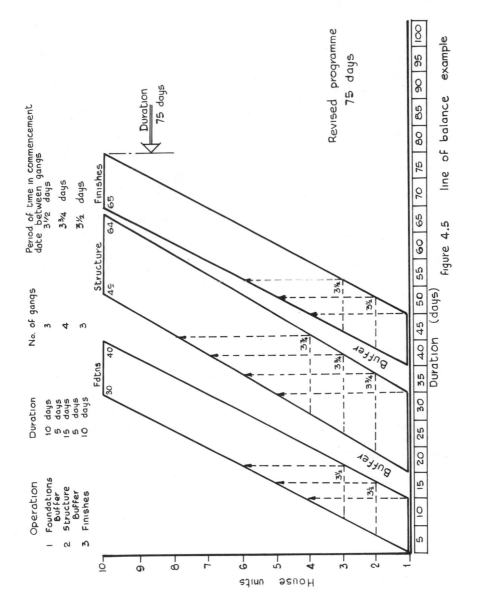

Figure 4.5   line of balance example

(1) Only applicable to repetitive forms of construction, e.g. houses and flats.

(2) Summarises many considerations, thus short of detail and hence explanation.

4.1.9 Application of Line of Balance

The technique was originally developed by the National Building Agency[1] for planning and controlling mass production processes in factories by determining the resources and speed of each stage of manufacture so that a required rate of output could be achieved. It appeared perhaps that repetitive construction such as building a number of similar houses has much in common with factory production.

The planning system is suitable for housing contracts, joinery works and the erection of prefabricated buildings. The process may also be applied to any sequence involving the co-ordination of a number of repetitive trade operations.

4.1.10 The Critical Path Method - Network Analysis
Format of Presentation

The programme may be presented as a network diagram showing earliest and latest event times and the critical path as in Figure 4.6. Alternatively the network can be presented to a time or calendar scale in the form of a bar chart in Figure 4.7 or as a time-scaled network in Figure 4.8.

For the larger, more complex project a computer analysis may be adopted. With network planning, time is of the essence, the principle being to complete the task in the shortest possible time taking into account the available resources. Dependencies must be realistic.

It is essential that site management personnel responsible for implementing the contract planning procedures have knowledge of the principles of network planning and understand the basic terminology used.

4.1.11 Advantages of the Critical Path Method

(1) Requires the planner to think logically.

(2) Activities upon which the contractor must concentrate his efforts during the project are identified in the process of planning.

(3) Non-critical activities are also identified and resource levelling is facilitated.

Station Project

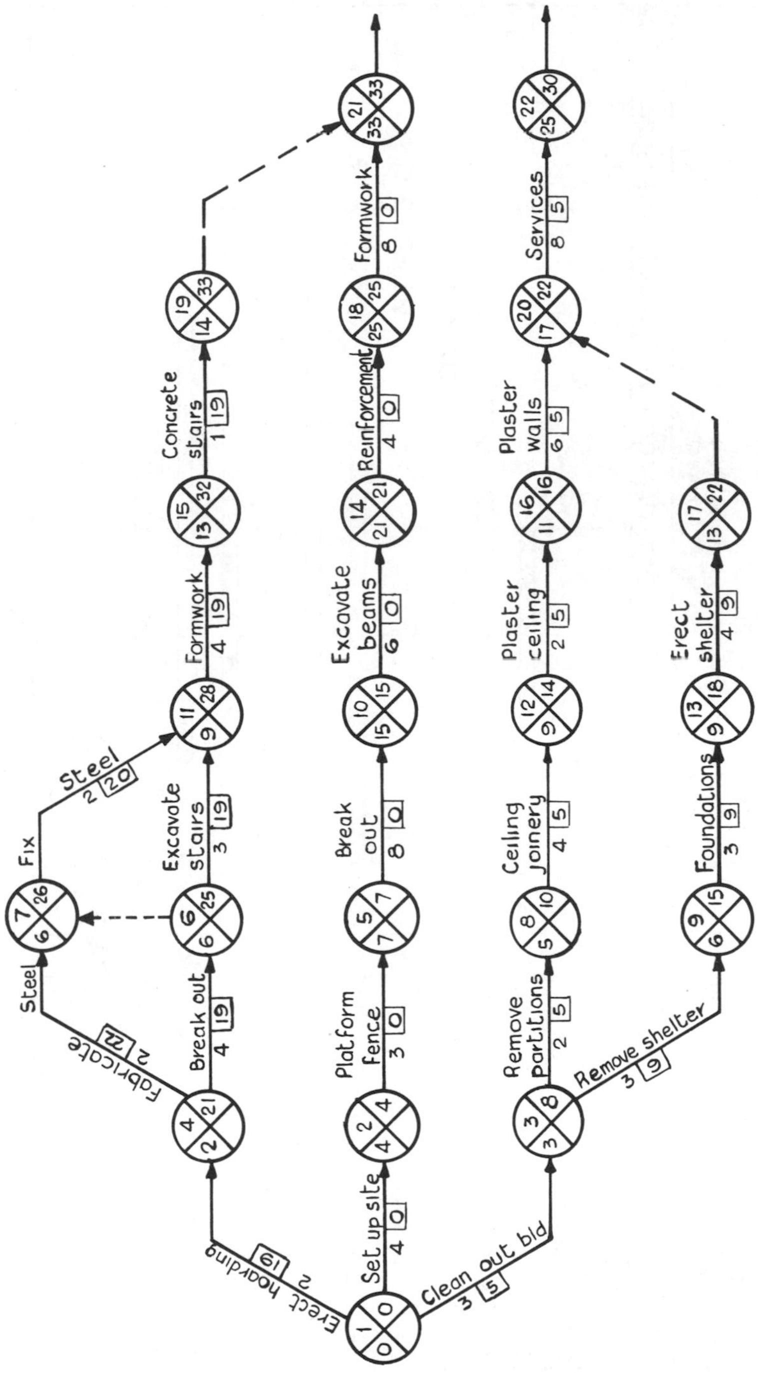

figure 4.6 network analysis example

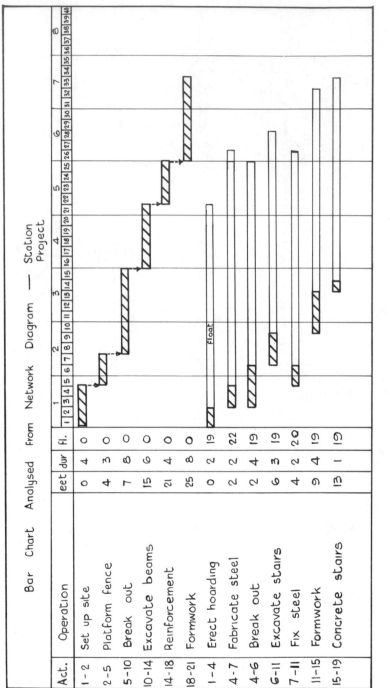

Bar Chart Analysed From Network Diagram — Station Project

Act.	Operation	eet	dur	Fl.	1 2 3 4 5 6 7 8 9 10 11 12 13 14 15 16 17 18 19 20 21 22 23 24 25 26 27 28 29 30 31 32 33 34 35 36 37 38 39 40
1-2	Set up site	0	4	0	
2-5	Platform fence	4	3	0	
5-10	Break out	7	8	0	
10-14	Excavate beams	15	6	0	
14-18	Reinforcement	21	4	0	
18-21	Formwork	25	8	0	
1-4	Erect hoarding	0	2	19	Float
4-7	Fabricate steel	2	2	22	
4-6	Break out	2	4	19	
6-11	Excavate stairs	6	3	19	
7-11	Fix steel	4	2	20	
11-15	Formwork	9	4	19	
15-19	Concrete stairs	13	1	19	

Figure 4.7   bar chart developed from network

138

Time Scaled Network ——— Station Project																															
week 1					week 2					week 3					week 4					week 5					week 6						
4ᵗʰ	5ᵗʰ	6ᵗʰ	7ᵗʰ	8ᵗʰ	11	12	13	14	15	18	19	20	21	22	25	26	27	28	29	1	2	3	4	5	8	9	10	11	12	15	16
1	2	3	4	5	6	7	8	9	10	11	12	13	14	15	16	17	18	19	20	21	22	23	24	25	26	27	28	29	30	31	32

Set up site → Fence → Break out → Excavate beams → Reinforcement → Formwork →

Clean out → Ptns → Ceiling Joinery → Plaster clgs → Plaster walls → Float – – →

Remove shelter → Foundations → Erect shelter → – Float – – – – →

Labour resources

| 1 | 2 | 3 | 4 | 5 | 6 | 7 | 8 | 9 | 10 | 11 | 12 | 13 | 14 | 15 | 16 | 17 | 18 | 19 | 20 | 21 | 22 | 23 | 24 | 25 | 26 | 27 | 28 | 29 | 30 | 31 | 32 |

Joiners — Ptns | Ceiling | Ceiling joinery | Remove shelter | Foundation | Erect shelter { Joiners moved from partitions & ceiling to shelter — 9 days. Float utilised

figure 4.8   time   scaled   network

139

(4) Information and materials requirements, which act as restraints on the commencement of some activities, are identified in the process of planning.

(5) Arguments in support of claims can be developed where some action on the part of the client or his advisers delays a critical activity.

(6) Crash times - alternative durations based on increased gang sizes - may be introduced in order to recover lost ground.

(7) The network may be translated onto a time or calendar scale in order to level resources by manual adjustment (as opposed to computer updating). In this form it has many advantages of the bar chart but easily becomes complex and obscure.

(8) Alternative resource levels may be considered by running a computer programme for different activity durations. This can be determined from alternative levels of manning in order to determine the least cost and shortest contract duration.

4.1.12 Disadvantages

(1) Not readily understood as a graphical statement of the contract duration.

(2) Updating calls for a redrafted network from the date concerned. Frequent updating entails continuous redrafting in a situation of uncertainty and becomes remote from managerial decision making.

(3) Contract information and drawings rarely go without amendment after work starts on site. Information not available to the contractor prior to the preparation of the network. may then itself initiate programme updating.

(4) A thorough knowledge of the construction process and of practical sequences is required prior to preparing the network. This will involve liaison between site management and the planner preparing the network. This liaison facility is rarely available.

4.1.13 Application of Networks

A survey undertaken by Oxley and Thompson[2] investigated the application of networks in the industry. It was found that critical path analysis had found the most use where size and complexity of project rendered bar charts inadequate. In other cases network planning was imposed on the contractor by the contractural terms.

The survey indicated that there was a marked reluctance by site staff to use anything other than bar charts. Most companies have adopted the planning system that works best for them, whether it be bar charts, networks or line of balance techniques. In recent years there has been increasing use of precedence networks in preference to arrow diagrams.

The main reasons given for not using networks are

(1) Better methods available for certain types of construction e.g. line of balance for repetitive construction.

(2) Bar charts are adequate for simple projects.

(3) Networks are more difficult and costly to update than bar charts and the supposed benefits are not achieved in practice.

(4) Difficulty in implementation at site level where the bar chart is assumed to be superior.

To combine the planning advantages of critical path analysis with the visual appeal of bar charts for use on site, some planners have developed logic linked bar charts.

Despite the problems, however, there is little doubt that the industry has benefited from the introduction of critical path techniques.

4.2 PROGRAMME SEQUENCE FOR A HOUSING CONTRACT

An assessment is required of the labour resources for undertaking the construction of twenty detached houses on a high quality development.

Manning levels are to be assessed for general labour, bricklayers and joinery gangs which are to be directly engaged on the contract.

The operations and durations to be programmed are as follows

Operation	Duration
Site clearance	$\frac{1}{2}$ week
Excavate and concrete foundations	1 week
Brickwork to d.p.c.	1 week
Services to ground floor	$\frac{1}{2}$ week
Hardcore and concrete ground floor slab	$\frac{1}{2}$ week
External brickwork	4 weeks
Roof and fascia construction	1 week
Roof tiling	$\frac{1}{2}$ week
First fixing - joinery	$1\frac{1}{2}$ weeks

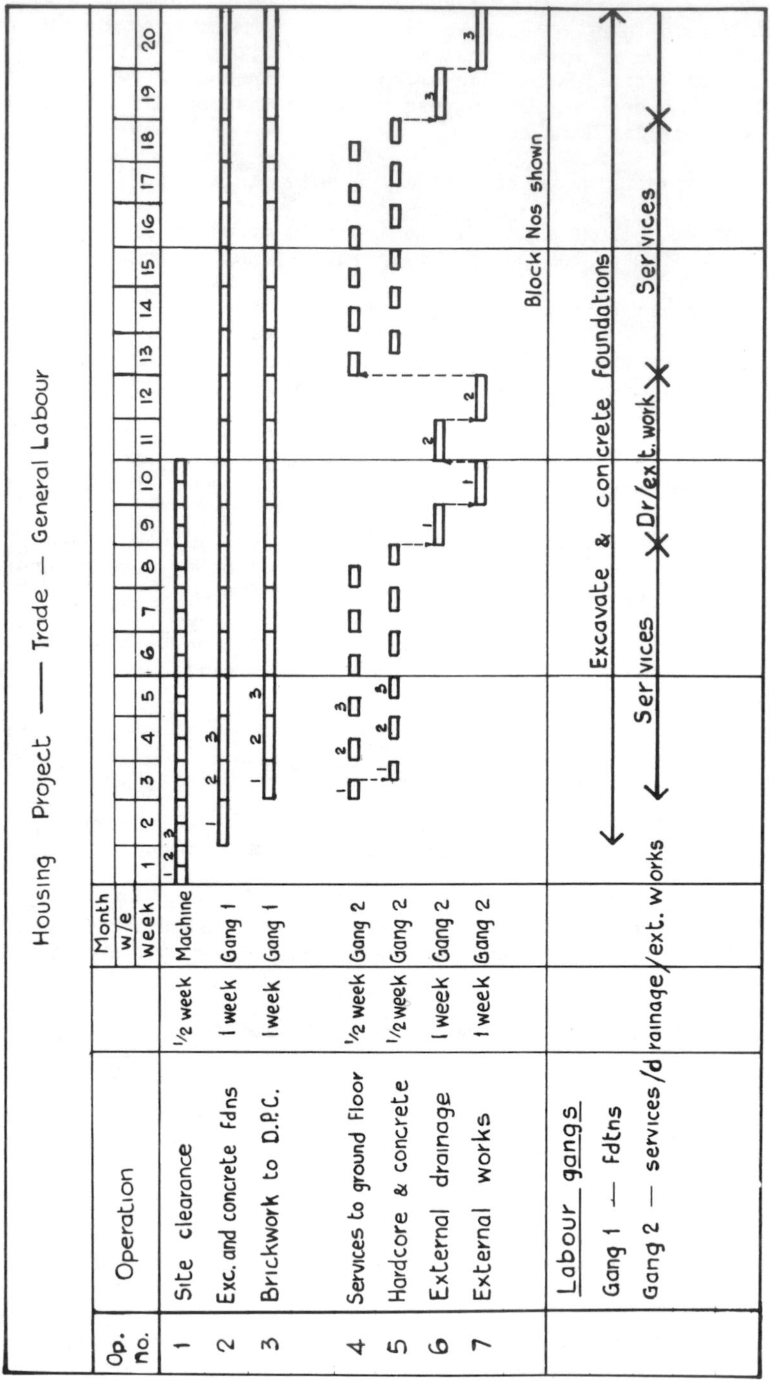

Housing Project —— Trade — General Labour

Figure 4.9   contract programme

4.2.1 Points to be Considered to Enable Continuity of Work for
       Operatives

(1) General labour gangs may be moved from foundation work to
     drainage and external works operations.   This will assist
     in ensuring continuity of work ensuring the sequence of
     undertaking the external works is not carried out too early
     in the sequence.   Work may be completed on up to six house
     foundations prior to commencing the external works.   A
     sequence for labour gangs is illustrated in Figure 4.9.

(2) Bricklaying operations may be based on a one gang, one
     block basis, e.g. bricklayers gang one, working on the
     foundations and superstructure on the same block and then
     moving to the next unit.   When the second house is to be
     commenced, the operation may be delayed until the first
     gang is available or an additional gang of bricklayers
     introduced.   In this way two gangs of bricklayers will
     construct alternate house units.

(3) It may prove advantageous to use one gang of bricklayers
     constructing all the foundation works, for example where
     foundation works are to be laid down before the onset of
     the winter months.   A sequence study illustrating the
     movement of brickwork gangs is illustrated in Figure 4.10.

(4) With roof carpentry work and roof tiling operations it
     may prove advantageous to have two roofs ready for tiling
     at one time.   This will reduce the number of visits to
     site by the tiling subcontractor.   The carpenters may
     then be moved on to first fix joinery work in order to
     provide continuity of work.   The relationship between
     roof construction, tiling and first fixing operations is
     illustrated in Figure 4.11.

     An extract from the overall programme is indicated in
     Figure 4.12.

(5) Various alternatives are available for consideration
     depending upon the number of trade gangs engaged on the
     contract.   Manning levels are dependent upon the avail-
     ability of labour within the contractor's organisation or
     the free availability of labour-only subcontractors.
     Sequence studies may be prepared on site by the site
     manager or site planning engineer in order to aid short
     term planning procedures.   In this way the various alter-
     native manning levels may be matched and the overall
     sequence of operations decided upon.

Housing Project ——— Trade —— Bricklayers

Op. no.	Operation	Month w/e week	1	2	3	4	5	6	7	8	9	10	11	12	13	14	15	16	17	18	19	20
1	Brickwork to D.P.C.	Gang 1																				
2	Brickwork to ext. walls	Gang 2																				
		Gang 3																				
	Alternative																					
	Brickwork to D.P.C.	Gang 1																				
	External brickwork	Gang 2																				
	Labour gangs for alternative																					
	Gang 1 — fdtns & ext. walls																					
	Gang 2 — fdtns & ext. walls																					

— Continuity for 20 units

Ditto 10 units

Ditto 10 units

Block 1, Block 2, Block 3, Block 4, Block 5, Block 6

Block Nos shown

figure 4.10   contract programme

144

Housing Project — Trade — Joinery

Op. no.	Operation	w/e	Month week 1	2	3	4	5	6	7	8	9	10	11	12	13	14	15	16	17	18	19	20
1	Roof construction	1 week	Gang 1		Full continuity																	
2	Roof tiling	½ week	S/C																			
3	First fix joinery	1 week	Gang 1																			
4	Plastering	2 week	S/C	Full continuity																		
5	Final fix joinery	2 week	Gang 2	Full continuity																		

Block Nos shown

Gang schedule

Joiners — gang 1	Roof and 1st Fix	2 joiners
Joiners — gang 2	Final Fix	2 joiners
Roof tilers	S/C	2 tilers
Plasterers	S/C	2 plasterers

Blocks 1 & 2   Blocks 3 & 4   Blocks 5 & 6
Blocks 1 to 10
1 & 2   3 & 4   5 & 6
Blocks 1 to 10

figure 4.11   contract programme

145

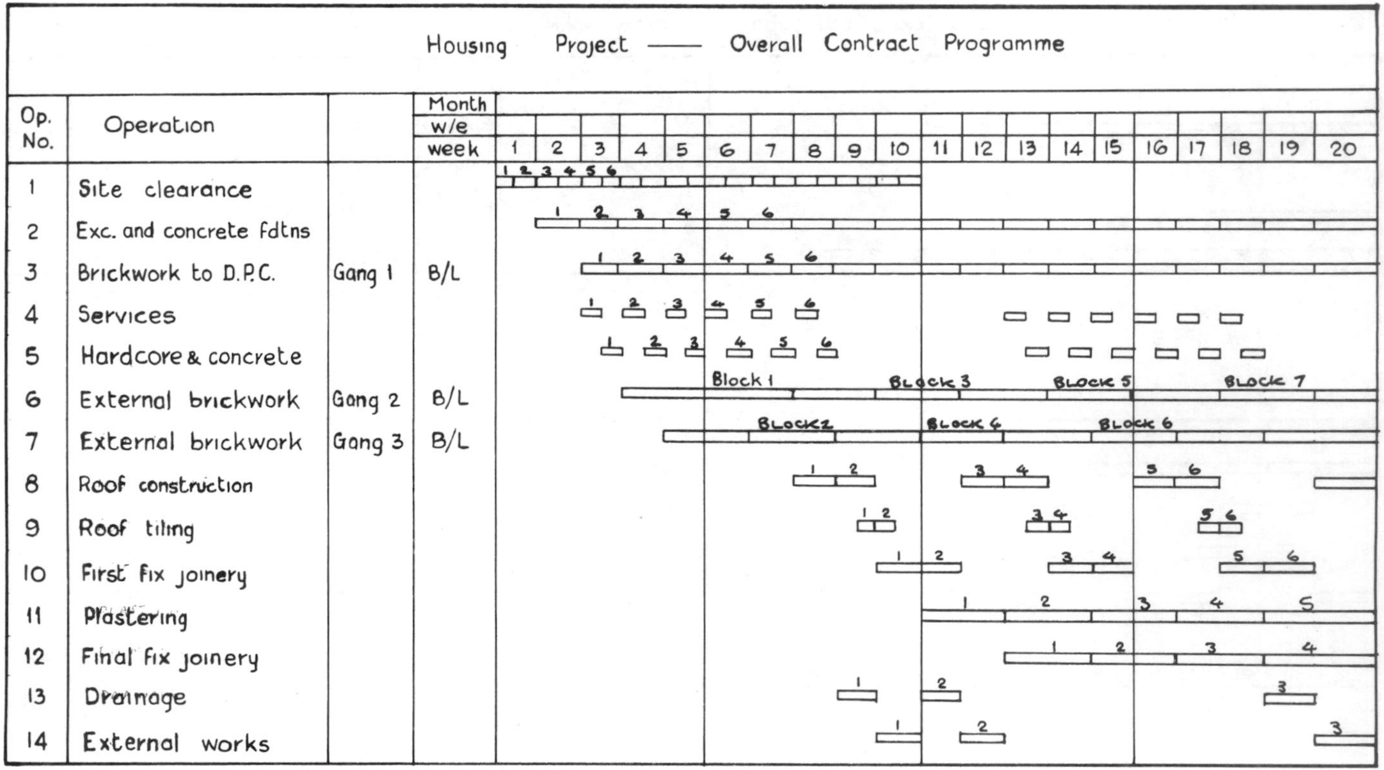

Housing Project — Overall Contract Programme

Figure 4.12 ` contract programme

4.3 PROGRAMME SEQUENCE FOR THE ERECTION OF TWENTY-FOUR REINFORCED CONCRETE COLUMNS

A sequence study is to be prepared for the construction of twenty-four reinforced concrete columns for a hangar building (see Figure 4.13).   The following sequence of construction has been determined.

	Operation	Duration per two columns
(1)	Excavate bases	1 day
(2)	Concrete blinding	$\frac{1}{2}$ day
(3)	Reinforcement to base	1 day
(4)	Concrete bases	1 day
(5)	Reinforcement to columns	1 day
(6)	Formwork to columns	2 days
(7)	Concrete columns	1 day
(8)	Striking formwork	1 day

The duration of each operation has been based on a practical assessment for each pair of columns.   This allows for six formwork uses prior to partial remaking.

4.3.1 Sequence of Operations and Methods of Construction

(1) Excavate bases
Bases to be excavated using an hydraulic backactor or multi-purpose wheeled excavator.   Part to be carted away, remainder to be tipped adjacent to base for backfilling. Quantity of excavation per base approximately 23 m^3. Work to the bases may proceed at two bases per day.   No earth support allowed as site report indicates good ground conditions.

(2) Concrete blinding to bases
Blinding to be undertaken on completion of excavation to each pair of bases.

(3) Reinforcement to bases
Base reinforcement and starter bars to follow blinding operation.

(4) Concrete to bases
Direct discharge into bases from ready mixed concrete lorry.   Kicker to be formed on base slab prior to erecting reinforcement and formwork.

(5) Reinforcement to columns
Reinforcement may be prefabricated adjacent to bases and lifted into position by crane.   Reinforcement to be completed prior to erecting formwork.

(6) Formwork to columns
Patent formwork with metal strongbacks to be used. Crane to be used for handling formwork into position.

147

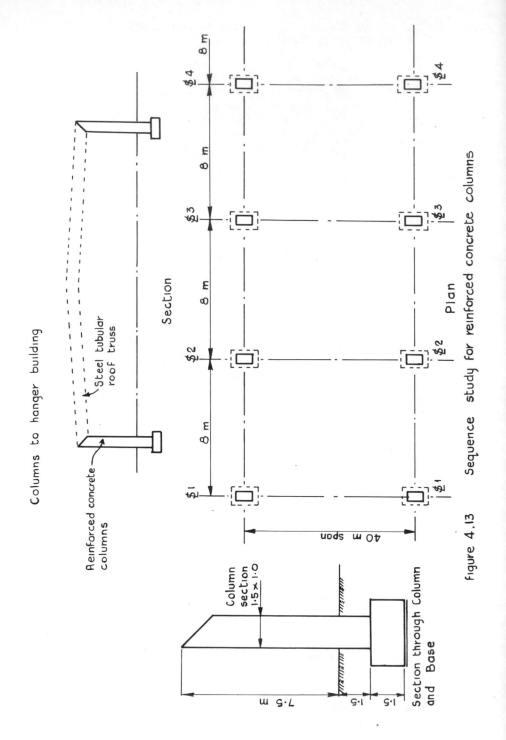

Columns to hanger building

Section

Plan

Section through Column and Base

Figure 4.13 Sequence study for reinforced concrete columns

(7) Concrete to columns
   Ready mixed concrete to be handled by crane and skips.
   Formwork to incorporate access scaffold for labour util-
   isation during concreting.

(8) Striking formwork
   Bolts and cramps to be eased by carpenters and formwork
   to be removed by crane assistance.

4.3.2 Continuity of Work

Excavation, blinding, reinforcement and concrete to bases may proceed in sequence.   Reinforcement to columns may then follow.

   One gang of carpenters may then be used for erecting the column
formwork, standing by on the concreting operations and then striking
the column shutters and moving to the next fixing position.   Figure 4.14 indicates a sequence study for the erection of the columns.

   As an alternative, four column shutters may be used to provide
full continuity of work for two gangs of carpenters as illustrated
in Case 2 on the programme.

4.3.3 Objectives of Preparing Sequence Studies

Sequence studies may be prepared at site management level in order
to compare the alternative use of resources of men, materials and
plant.

   The amount of formwork to be utilised directly affects the speed
of the operation and the number of gangs to be employed.   Sequence
studies assist in resolving problems involving balancing materials
and plant requirements with labour resources.

   By introducing an additional pair of column shutters full continuity of work for a carpentry gang can be achieved.   In this
way the gang are more economically engaged on productive work in
preference to acting on stand-by during concreting operations.
Where the planning system is productivity orientated, this
decision would affect the bonus earnings of the individual gang.

4.4 SHORT TERM PROGRAMME FOR A LABORATORY BLOCK

Eight laboratory blocks are to be fitted out and handed over on
completion.   It is assumed that the basic shell of the building
is complete including glazing.

   The order of work in each laboratory is indicated together
with the man-hour allocation.

Sequence Study ———— Erection of 24 Columns

Op. no.	Operation	Dur. days	1	2	3	4	5	6	7	8	9	10	11	12	13	14	15	16	17	18	19	20	21	22	23	24	25
1	Excavate base	1																									
2	Reinforcement	1																									
3	Concrete base	1																									
4	Column reinforcement	1																									
5	Column Formwork	2																									
6	Concrete column	1																									
7	Strike Formwork	1																									
	Alternative — case ii																										
8	Column Formwork	2																									
9	Concrete columns	1																									
10	Strike Formwork	1																									
	Labour resources — case ii																										
	Carpenters - gang 1																										
	Carpenters - gang 2																										

Case 1 sufficient column shutters for 2 No. columns (1 pair)

4 No. column shutters available (2 pair)

Column Formwork moved from $1 to $3

Similar procedure on $2 & $4

Day 18

$1 $2 $3 $4 $5 $6

Figure 4.14   sequence study

150

Op. No.	Operation	Man-hours allocated	Trade
1.	Plastering to walls	96	Plasterers, s/c.
2.	Fix suspended ceilings	48	Ceiling fixers, s/c.
3.	Fix benches up to walls	128	Joiners
4.	Services to benches – Electrical	48	Electricians
5.	Floor tiling between benches	64	Floor tilers, s/c.
6.	Internal painting	48	Painters
7.	Clean out and hand over	48	Labourers

s/c. indicates subcontract trades

An extract from the short term programme is to be prepared together with operational time calculations to show the number of operatives to be engaged on the contract. Continuity of trades must be aimed at for both the contractors' own labour and the labour engaged by the subcontractors.

4.4.1 Programme Calculations

A programme calculation sheet is shown. This allows the duration of each operation to be matched.

Programme Calculation Sheet

Op. No.	Operation	Man-hours	Man-days ($\div$8 h.)	Gang size	Gang duration
1.	Plastering	96	12	3 plasterers	4 days
2.	Suspended ceilings	48	6	2 fixers	3 days
3.	Fix benches	128	16	4 joiners	4 days
4.	Services	48	6	2 electricians	3 days
5.	Floor tiling	64	8	2 tilers	4 days
6.	Internal painting	48	6	2 painters	3 days
7.	Clean out	48	6	2 labourers	3 days

4.4.2 Presentation of the Short Term Programme

A short term programme indicating the sequence of operations for the eight laboratory blocks is indicated in Figure 4.15.

Continuity of work has been achieved for the plastering, fixing benches and floor tiling. The remaining operations have been organised in two visits. By delaying the commencement of say, the suspended ceilings by three days, continuity work on four laboratory units can be obtained. A similar delayed start may be applied to the services and internal painting operations.

151

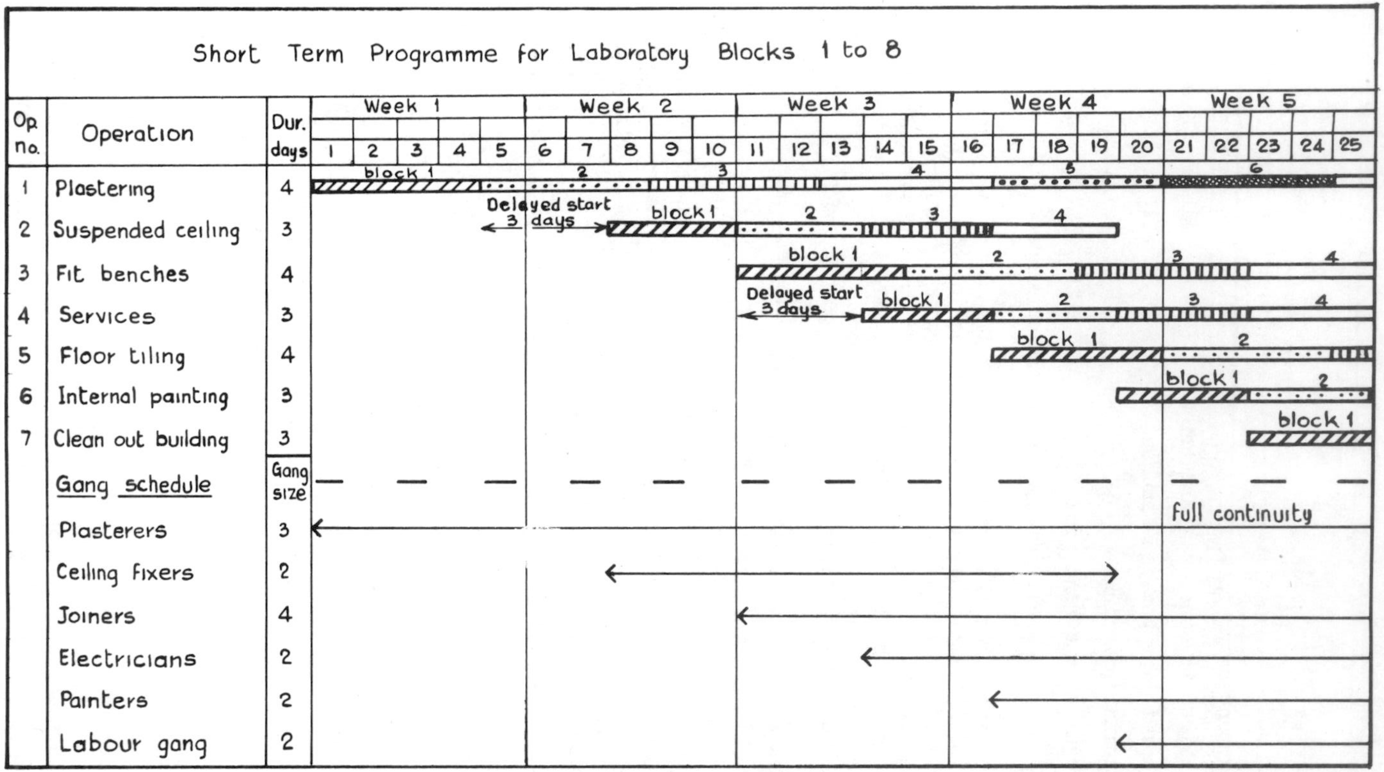

Short Term Programme for Laboratory Blocks 1 to 8

Op. no.	Operation	Dur. days	Week 1	Week 2	Week 3	Week 4	Week 5
			1 2 3 4 5	6 7 8 9 10	11 12 13 14 15	16 17 18 19 20	21 22 23 24 25
1	Plastering	4	block 1				
2	Suspended ceiling	3		Delayed start 3 days → block 1			
3	Fit benches	4			block 1		
4	Services	3			Delayed start 3 days block 1		
5	Floor tiling	4				block 1	
6	Internal painting	3					block 1
7	Clean out building	3					block 1
	Gang schedule	Gang size					
	Plasterers	3					full continuity
	Ceiling fixers	2					
	Joiners	4					
	Electricians	2					
	Painters	2					
	Labour gang	2					

figure 4.15 Short term programme

4.5 NETWORK PROGRAMME FOR A BRIDGE PROJECT

An advanced bridge is to be constructed for a motorway project and the following activities, durations and sequence of work have been established.

An elevation and section of the proposed bridge is indicated in Figure 4.16.

Activity	Duration	
Site strip - complete bridge	4 days	
Pier A		
Excavate pier	3 days	
Blinding to pier	1 day	
Fix reinforcement and formwork to kicker	3 days	Repeat acti-
Concrete pier foundation	1 day	vities on
Reinforcement to abutment	4 days	deck between
Fix formwork	5 days	piers B and C
Concrete abutment	1 day	
Strip formwork	2 days	
Deck slab (piers A to B)		
Fix precast concrete beams	1 day	
Fix formwork to deck	5 days	Repeat
Fabricate and fix reinforcement	3 days	activities
Concrete deck	1 day	on deck
Strip formwork to deck	2 days	between
Curing period prior to striking formwork	7 days	piers
		B and C

4.5.1 Resources to be Allocated - Case 1

The following resources of temporary works and plant are to be allocated for the bridge construction.

    One hydraulic excavator
    One pier shutter
    One set of formwork for the deck span between the piers

An assessment is required of the minimum construction period for the bridge project based on the above resources.

Figure 4.17 indicates a network diagram prepared for the project. Figure 4.18 shows this presented as a time-scaled diagram.

The analysis indicates a contract period of 69 days based on the resources available.

4.5.2 Alternative Considerations

The contractor is now to consider speeding up the construction programme. From the analysis of Case 1, the duration may be reduced by increasing the temporary works and plant resources for the project. This will also affect the utilisation of labour resources.

153

Publisher's note: this page has been left blank for technical reasons

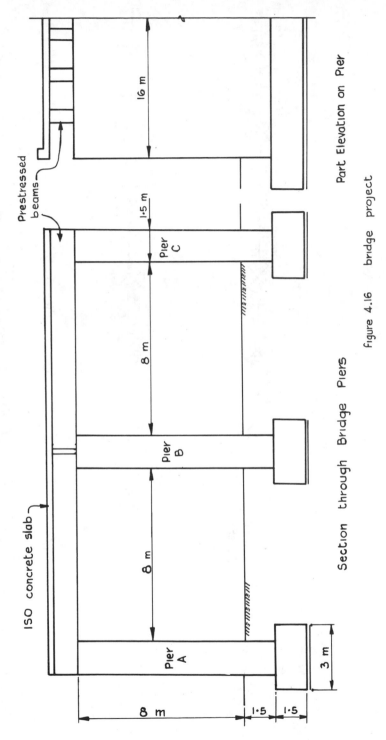

ISO concrete slab

Prestressed beams

16 m

Part Elevation on Pier

1·5 m

Pier
C

8 m

Pier
B

8 m

Pier
A

3 m

8 m

1·5   1·5

Section through Bridge Piers

Figure 4.16   bridge   project

Network Diagram — Case I Resources

Overall contract period

69 days

Resources : 1 no. excavator
1 no. pier shutter
½ bridge deck formwork

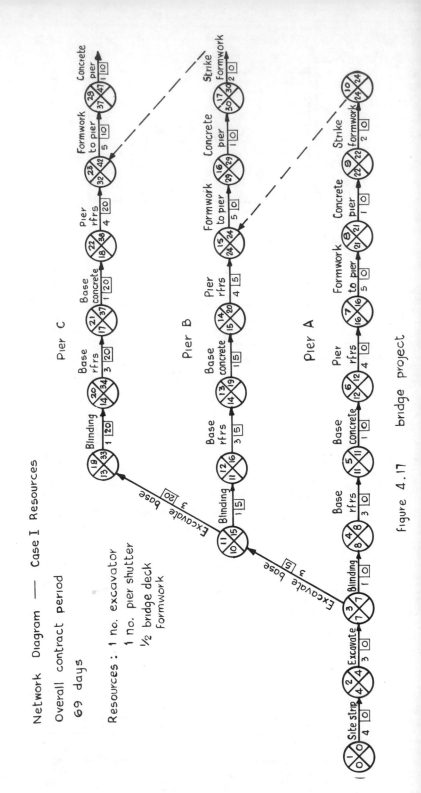

figure 4.17   bridge project

156

Network Diagram — Case I Resources

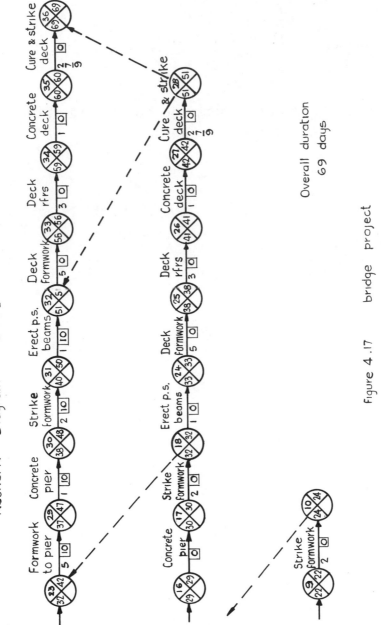

Figure 4.17   bridge project

Overall duration
69 days

157

Publisher's note: this page has been left blank for technical reasons

Time – scaled   Network —— Case I Resources

april					april					april					april					may					may					ma
3	4	5	6	7	10	11	12	13	14	17	18	19	20	21	24	25	26	27	28	1	2	3	4	5	8	9	10	11	12	15	16
1	2	3	4	5	6	7	8	9	10	11	12	13	14	15	16	17	18	19	20	21	22	23	24	25	26	27	28	29	30	31	32

Pier A

Strip site → Excavate → Blind → Base rfs → Conc. → Pier rfs → Formwork to pier → Conc. → Strike

Pier B → Excavate → Blind → Base rfs → Conc. → Pier rfs → Float — — → Formwork to pier → Conc. → Strike

Pier C → Excavate → Blind → Base rfs → Conc. → Pier rfs → Float — — →

Resources

1	2	3	4	5	6	7	8	9	10	11	12	13	14	15	16	17	18	19	20	21	22	23	24	25	26	27	28	29	30	31	32

Pier A   Pier B   Pier C

Reinforcement to piers	Pier A	Pier B	Pier C	Float on pier B & C utilised

figure 4.18   bridge project

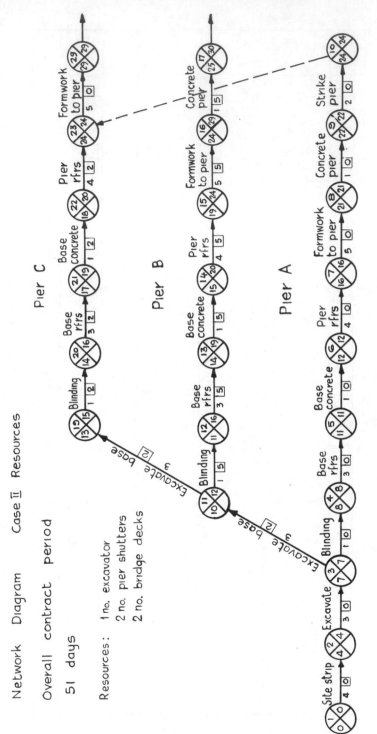

Network Diagram   Case II Resources

Overall contract period

51 days

Resources: 1 no. excavator
2 no. pier shutters
2 no. bridge decks

Pier C

Pier B

Pier A

Figure 4.19   bridge project

160

Network Diagram —— Case $\overline{II}$ Resources

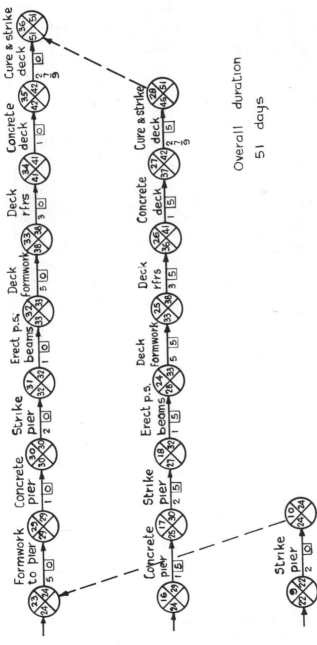
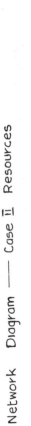

Overall duration

51 days

figure 4.19   bridge project

161

Time scaled Network   Case $\overline{\text{II}}$ Resources

april					april					april					april					may					may					ma
3	4	5	6	7	10	11	12	13	14	17	18	19	20	21	24	25	26	27	28	1	2	3	4	5	8	9	10	11	12	15	16
1	2	3	4	5	6	7	8	9	10	11	12	13	14	15	16	17	18	19	20	21	22	23	24	25	26	27	28	29	30	31	32

Pier A

Site strip → Excavate → Blind → Base rfs → Conc. → Pier rfs → Formwork to pier → Conc. → Strike

Pier B

Excavate → Blind → Base rfs → Conc. → Pier rfs → Formwork to pier → Conc. → Strike → Erect beams → Deck formwork

Pier C

Excavate → Blind → Base rfs → Conc. → Pier rfs → Float → Formwork to pier → Conc. → Strike

Resources

1	2	3	4	5	6	7	8	9	10	11	12	13	14	15	16	17	18	19	20	21	22	23	24	25	26	27	28	29	30	31	32

Base reinforcement gang 1   Pier A   Pier B   Pier C

Pier reinforcement gang 2   Pier A   Pier B   Pier C   Float on pier B&C utilised

figure 4.20   bridge   project

4.5.3 Proposals to Speed Up the Construction Programme

Increasing the following temporary works resources will reduce the overall contract period.

(1) Providing an additional pier shutter. In Case 1 a delay of 9 days occurs between fixing the pier reinforcement and erecting the formwork.

(2) Providing an additional deck shutter - again delays occur awaiting the striking of the first deck and its refixing between piers B and C. The utilisation of additional formwork will involve the employment of additional carpenters and a further steel-fixing gang.

4.5.4 Resources to be Allocated - Case 2

The following resources of temporary works and plant have been allocated and a revised network diagram for the project indicated in Figure 4.19. This is based on

> One hydraulic excavator
> Two pier shutters
> Two bridge decks

A time-scaled diagram for the revised project is illustrated in Figure 4.20 together with the revised labour resources.

4.5.5 Comparisons of Cases 1 and 2

The duration for the overall project has now been reduced to 51 days. Prior to finalising the decision for a reduced programme period a cost exercise must be undertaken in order to consider the economics of Cases 1 and 2. Although Case 2 is considerably shorter in duration the contractor is involved in the employment of additional labour gangs and the cost of additional formwork as well as a reduction in formwork utilisation.

4.6 NETWORK ANALYSIS - LEAD AND LAG TERMINOLOGY

Network planning techniques are based on the premise that one activity must be completed before the next one commences. In order to analyse a particular sequence of activities in more detail it may be necessary to develop subnetworks.

In order to express the relationship between the starting and completion dates of related activities which are carried out at the same time, lead and lag techniques may be introduced.

4.6.1 Lead and Lag Relationships

The erection of a steel portal frame for a factory project may lead the roof cladding activity by 10 days, i.e. the roof cladding may commence 10 days after the commencement of the steel erection.

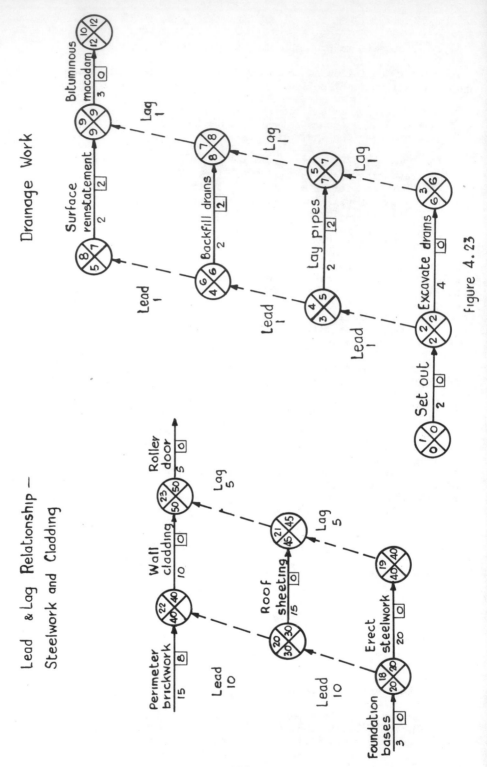

Drainage Work

Lead & Lag Relationship –
Steelwork and Cladding

figure 4.23

164

Bar Chart for Steelwork & Cladding

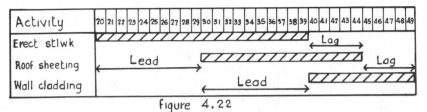

figure 4.22

Bar Chart — Drainage Work, Earliest Start Times

Activity	es	dur	fl	1	2	3	4	5	6	7	8	9	10	11	12
Set out	0	2	0												
Exc. drains	4	2	0												
Lay pipes	2	4	0												
Backfill drains	4	2	2												
Reinstatement	5	2	2												
Surfacing	9	3	0												

Earliest event times

figure 4.24

Bar Chart — Drainage work, Latest Start Times

Activity	es	dur	fl	1	2	3	4	5	6	7	8	9	10	11	12
Set out	0	2	0												
Exc. drains	2	4	0												
Lay pipes	4	2	2												
Backfill drains	4	2	2												
Reinstatement	5	2	2												
Surfacing	9	3	0												

Latest event times

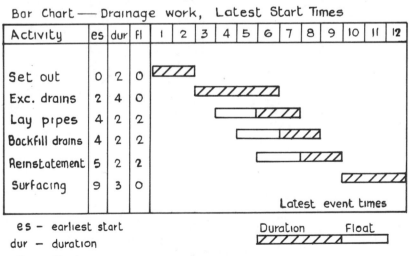

es — earliest start
dur — duration
fl — float

Duration   Float

figure 4.25

165

Network Diagram

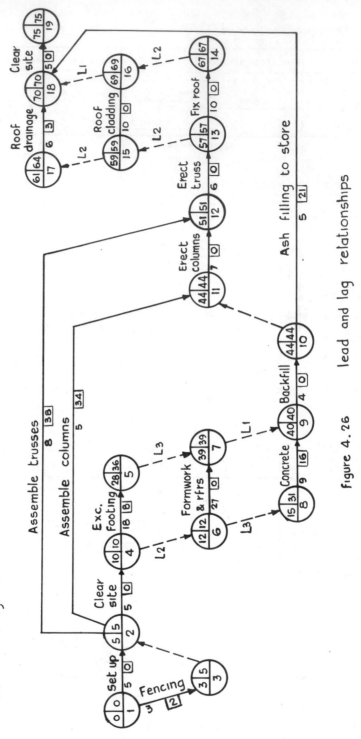

Figure 4.26   lead and lag relationships

166

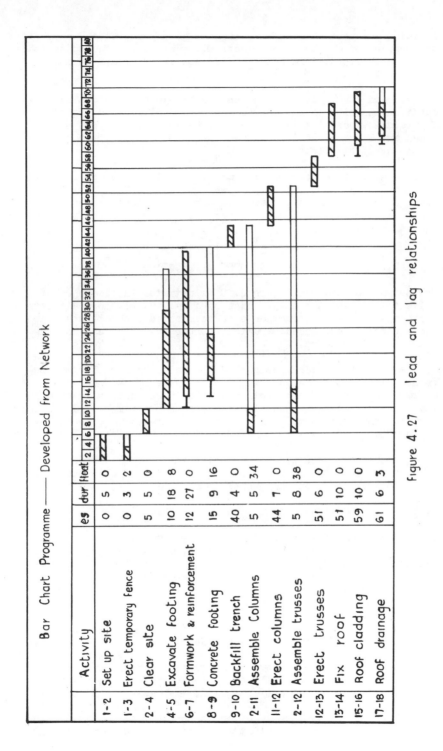

Bar Chart Programme —— Developed from Network

Figure 4.27 lead and lag relationships

Likewise the roof sheeting may require to be completed 5 days after the completion of the steel erection. This relationship is indicated in Figure 4.21 in network form and in bar chart form in Figure 4.22.

Lead and lag relationships can also be related to drainage excavation and pipe laying activities as illustrated in Figure 4.23. Figure 4.24 indicates the bar chart showing the earliest event times and Figure 4.25 illustrates the latest event times relative to the available float.

An example of a network diagram illustrating the application of lead and lag activities is shown in Figure 4.26. This has been analysed to indicate earliest and latest event times and the critical path. A bar chart prepared from the network is illustrated in Figure 4.27.

4.7 NETWORK ANALYSIS - CRASH COST APPLICATION

The network diagram in Figure 4.28 illustrates the sequence of activities during the first stage of a railway platform alteration. Work entails the construction of a reinforced concrete staircase and a concrete suspended structure consisting of bases, columns and first floor beams.

The network diagram in Figure 4.29 indicates normal times together with a cost assessment. On analysis it is found that overall duration of this section of the works must be reduced in time in order to meet a steelwork erection programme. The steelwork for the station building is to be delivered to site on day number 26.

Proposals are required for reducing the overall duration to 26 days in order to achieve the lowest crash cost situation and indicate the effect on the overall programme.

4.7.1 Crash Cost and Crash Times

The contractor may be required to reduce the overall time period on a series of related operations in order to meet a revised delivery date or simply to recover lost time. In these circumstances it is necessary to reconsider the programme in the short term in order that alternative resources of labour, materials and plant may be considered for the activities ahead.

A client may alternatively require the contractor to advance his completion date by say 10 to 15 days in order to gain early occupation of a factory or office block. In these cases the additional costs incurred by the contractor, in order to meet the revised programme dates, will be recoverable from the client. For this purpose least cost/crash time exercises can be undertaken.

The contractor will be required to consider all activities on the critical path in order that a reduction in the overall contract

Network Presentation for Normal Times

Contract period
normal time 32 days.

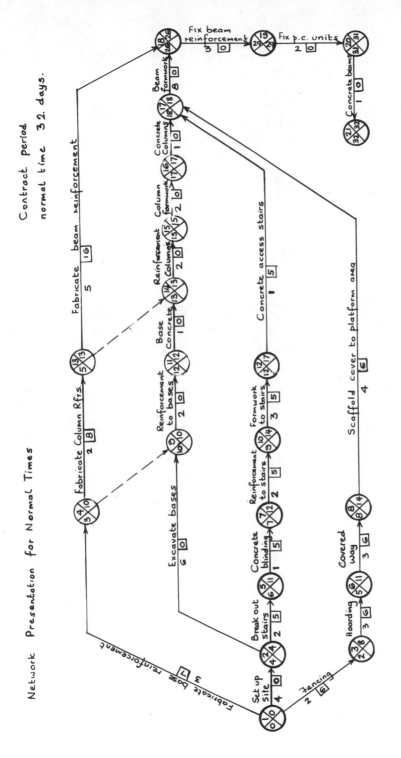

Figure 4.28 network diagram for railway platform work

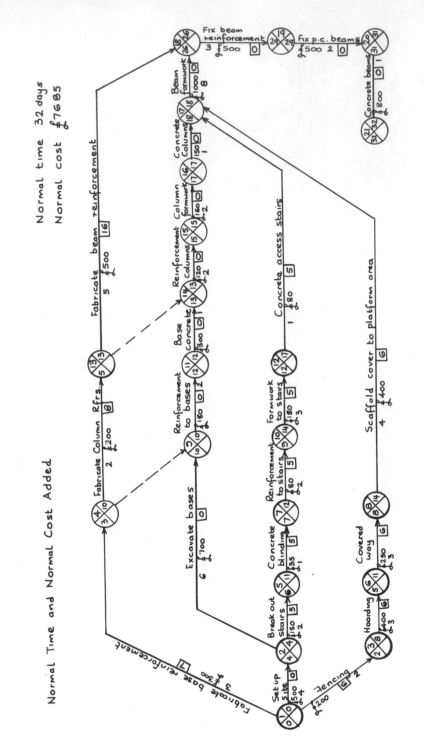

Normal Time and Normal Cost Added

Normal time 32 days
Normal cost £7685

Figure 4.29-31 network diagram for railway platform work

170

Activity	Normal time (days)	Normal cost (£)	Revised duration -crash time	Revised cost -crash cost	No. of days saved	Additional cost (£)	Additional cost per day saved (£)	Rank order	Float
Set up site	4	500	3	650	1	150	150		0
Break out stairs	3	150	2	250	1	100	100		4
Blinding	1	35	-	-	-	-	-		4
Reinforcements to stairs	2	80	1	130	1	50	50		4
Formwork to stairs	3	150	2	220	1	70	70		4
Concrete stairs	1	80	1	-	-	-	-		4
Excavate bases	6	700	3	1050	3	350	116	3rd	0
Fix base reinforcements	2	180	1	270	1	90	90	2nd	0
Concrete bases	1	300	-	-	-	-	-		0
Fix column reinforcements	2	120	1	180	1	60	60	1st	0
Concrete columns	1	150	-	-	-	-	-		0
Formwork to beams	8	1000	4	1600	4	600	150		0
Fix precast units	2	500	-	-	-	-	-		0
Fix reinforcement	3	500	2	650	1	150	150	4th	0
Concrete beams	1	500	-	-	-	-	-		0

6 days reduction

Figure 4.30

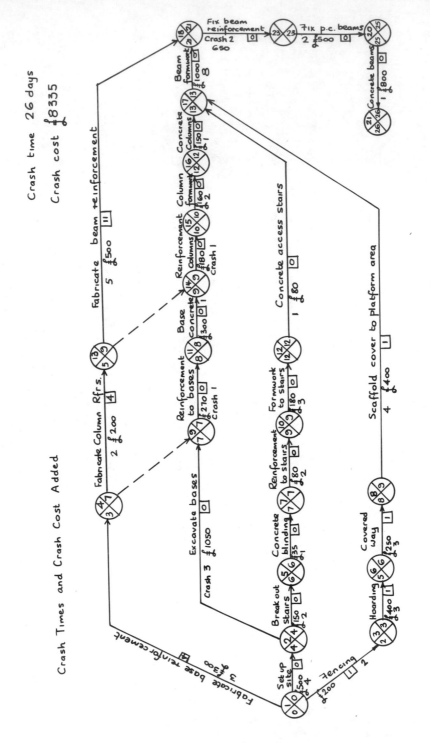

Crash Times and Crash Cost Added

Crash time 26 days

Crash cost £8335

figure 4.32 network diagram for railway platform work

172

period may be made.   Shortening non-critical activities will only
result in reducing floats.   These may however then become critical
and re-analysis of the network will be required in order to determine the new critical path.

A schedule of revised durations (crash times) and revised costs
(crash costs) should be prepared and the additional cost per day
saved assessed for each activity.   Figure 4.30 shows the data
analysed in schedule form.   Those activities with the least extra
cost for each day saved will normally be considered first, in rank
order, to assess the revised programme dates.

4.7.2 Analysis of the Network

Figure 4.31 indicates the network for the project analysed to show
normal times and cost.   The contract can be completed in 32 days
at a normal cost of £7685.   Figure 4.32 shows the revised network
analysed to indicate crash time and crash cost.   The project period
has been reduced to 26 days at a crash cost of £8335.   This has
been achieved by the following adjustments to the network.

Rank Order	Activity	Event No.	Reduction (days)	Cost per day £	Total
1	Fix column rfs.	14-15	1	60	60
2	Fix base rfs.	9-11	1	90	90
3	Excavate bases	2-9	3	116	350
4	Fix rfs. to beams	18-19	1	150	150
	Total reduction in time		6 days	Additional cost	£650

The analysis of the network for crash times shows that two
paths have now become critical, e.g. the base and column operations
together with the stairs sequence.   This has also affected the
float on the platform fencing and scaffold cover which has now
been reduced to one day.

Careful monitoring of the progress position on the critical
path will be required at site level.   Control must also be exercised on the base and column sequence as a delay of one day on
any of these activities will make the sequence critical.

4.8 PRECEDENCE DIAGRAMS - TERMINOLOGY AND RELATIONSHIPS

Various relationships between activities may be expressed by precedence diagrams which cannot readily be shown on network diagrams.
In order to outline these principles the fundamental relationships
and terminology used will be described.

173

4.8.1 Terminology and Analysis

Activities are indicated by boxes as shown in Figure 4.33 linked by lines or arrows to show relationships in the sequence. Activity numbers may be prefixed by a letter to show the element or trade to which they relate. This is useful for resourcing the different trade gangs at the resource allocation stage.

The method of analysis is similar to network analysis and the following procedures are undertaken in preparing and analysing the network.

(1) Prepare a list of activities indicating the relationships one with another.

(2) Present the activities in precedence diagram format and check the logic of the sequence. No dummies are needed to maintain the logic.

(3) Enter the activity numbers to suit the sequence/elements or trades.

(4) Apply the forward pass in order to calculate the earliest starts and earliest finishes.

(5) Determine the overall project time.

(6) Apply the backward pass to calculate the latest finish and latest start times.

Those activity modes with equal earliest and latest start times together with earliest and latest finish times are critical to the sequence of the precedence diagram. Account must be taken of the start and finish relationships which exist between related activities.

4.8.2 Relationships Used on Precedence Diagrams

Finish to start relationships are shown in Figure 4.34.

Lag finish to start relationships may be introduced to show delays between the completion of one activity and the start of the next. Figure 4.35 illustrates this applied to the curing of a suspended deck slab and the striking of formwork.

Start to start relationships indicate activities which commence at the same time as shown in Figure 4.36.

Lag starts are introduced to show overlaps between the commencement of related activities. Figure 4.37 illustrates the relationship between the commencement of the road base construction and the laying of land drains to an adjacent wall.

Finish to finish relationships indicate activities which all finish at the same time as shown in Figure 4.38.

174

Precedence Networks

Latest start time ⟶ 10   16 ⟵ Latest finish time

Earliest start time ⟶ 10   16 ⟵ Earliest finish time

Description ⟶ Clear site

Duration ⟶ 6   e4 ⟵ Activity number

Earliest finish = earliest start + duration

Latest start = latest finish − duration

figure 4.33   terminology

Precedence Network

Finish to start relationship — floor slab can not start until foundations are complete.

Procurement symbols may be introduced relating to key material requirements

Denotes first activity in a chain

⟵ Procurement symbol

32   42
0   10
Procure slab reinforcement
10   P6

22   42
10   30
Construct foundations
20   F8

42   52
30   40
Floor slab
10   F9

Finish to start relationship

figure 4.34   terminology

175

Precedence Networks

Main setting out can start at the same time as the setting up of the site accommodation but not before

Start to start relationship

figure 4.36   terminology

Precedence Networks

Denotes normal delay between activities. Formwork cannot be stripped until 10 days after concreting is completed. This period may be for the curing of the concrete slab

Lag finish to start relationship

Figure 4.35   terminology

Precedence Networks

Construction of road sub-base cannot start until 9 days after commencement of the land drain to the retaining wall

Prefix to activity numbers

Pr— preliminaries
F — foundations
D— drainage
R— road
E — excavation
C— concrete
Fo— formwork
P— procurement

Lag start relationship

figure 4.37   terminology

Precedence Networks

Fill to tip cannot finish until excavation in bulk is complete e.g. both activities finish at the same time

Finish to finish relationship

figure 4.38   terminology

177

Precedence Networks

Clearing of site cannot finish until 4 days after seeding the embankment is complete

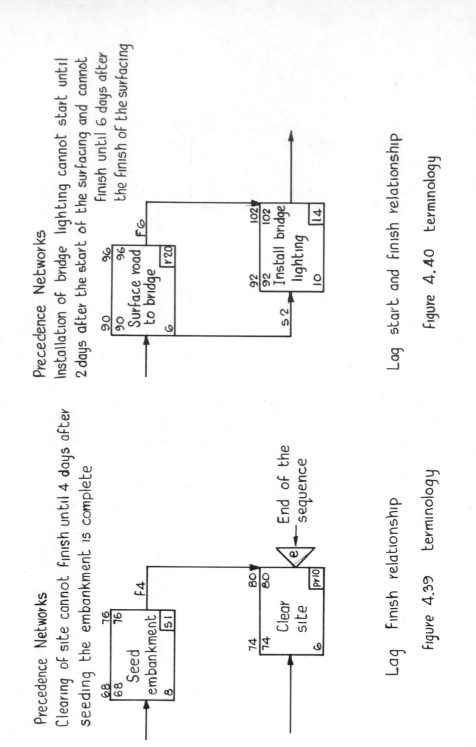

Lag finish relationship

Figure 4.39 terminology

Precedence Networks

Installation of bridge lighting cannot start until 2 days after the start of the surfacing and cannot finish until 6 days after the finish of the surfacing

Lag start and finish relationship

Figure 4.40 terminology

178

Precedence Networks

Subnetwork for construction
of pier

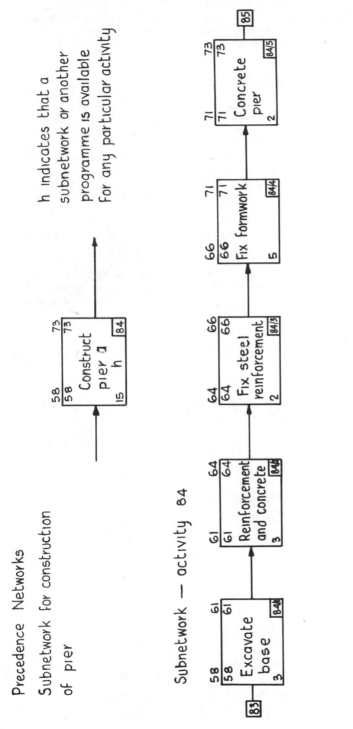

h indicates that a
subnetwork or another
programme is available
for any particular activity

Subnetwork — activity 84

figure 4.41   terminology

179

inish relationships relate to overlaps which occur between
letion of related activities. Figure 4.39 indicates that
cannot be cleared until four days after the completion of
nt seeding.

start and finish relationships relate to overlap at both
the beginning and end of related activities. Figure 4.40 indicates that the installation of bridge lighting cannot start until
two days after the commencement of surfacing and cannot finish
until six days after the completion of surfacing.

Hammock activities and subnetworks may be introduced to allow
the detailed analysis of a single activity to be developed.
Figure 4.41 shows a subnetwork for the detailed construction of
a pier. The subnetwork is linked to the main precedence diagram
by continuity boxes as illustrated.

Processment symbols may be introduced and linked in at relevant
stages of the precedence diagram. This allows the purchasing of
key materials to be directly linked to the activity and enables
key dates to be assessed for the placing of orders and the delivery
of materials to site. Specified date symbols can be introduced
which relate to calendar dates or the day for the start or finish
of any key activity.

4.9 PRECEDENCE NETWORKS – CASE STUDY

4.9.1

A precedence network for the construction of a single-storey in
situ concrete framed building is illustrated in the case study.

Activity No.	Activity	Duration	Relationship
E1	Excavate foundations	10 days	
E1	Construct foundations	20 days	
D1	Excavate and lay drains	6 days	
D2	Backfill to drains	2 days	
F1	Construct column and beams to roof level	30 days	
E3	Construct ground floor slab	10 days	
F2	Erect precast roof units	5 days	
F3	Screed and finish to roof units	8 days	
B1	External brickwork and metal windows	15 days	
I1	Internal finishes	20 days	
D3	Landscape and topsoil	5 days	

180

Predence Diagram for an
In Situ Concrete Frame

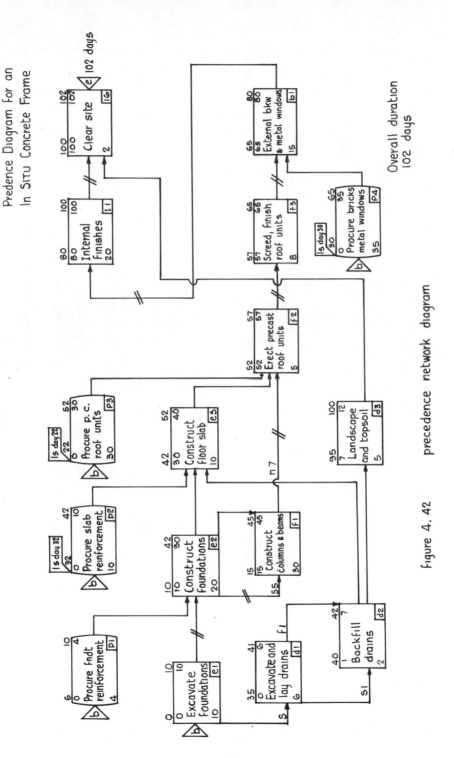

Overall duration
102 days

Figure 4.42   precedence network diagram

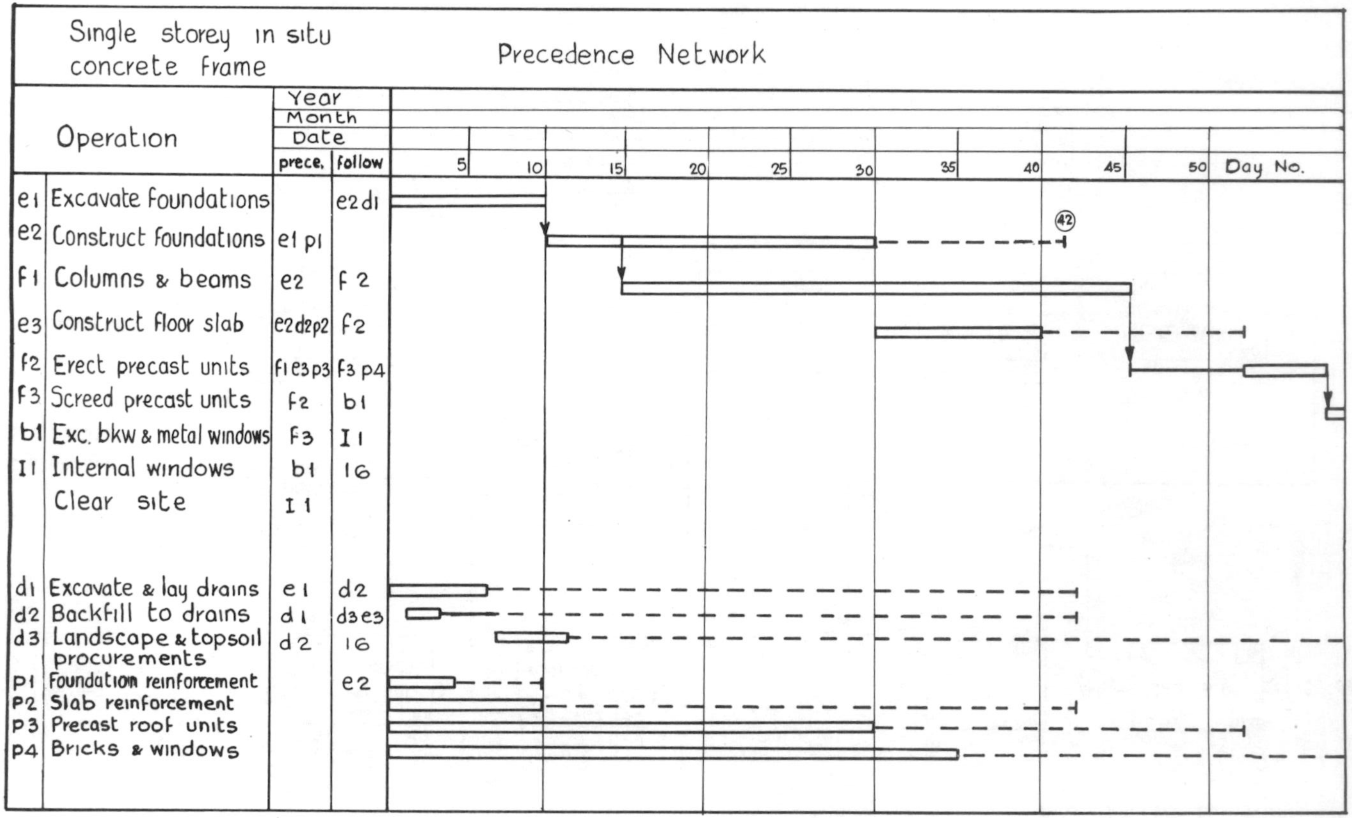

Single storey in situ concrete frame
Precedence Network
Operation
Year
Month
Date
prece.
follow
5
10
15
20
25
30
35
40
45
50
Day No.
42
e1 Excavate foundations e2 d1
e2 Construct foundations e1 p1
f1 Columns & beams e2 f 2
e3 Construct floor slab e2 d2 p2 f2
f2 Erect precast units f1 e3 p3 f3 p4
f3 Screed precast units f2 b1
b1 Exc. bkw & metal windows f3 I 1
I1 Internal windows b1 16
Clear site I 1
d1 Excavate & lay drains e 1 d2
d2 Backfill to drains d 1 d3 e3
d3 Landscape & topsoil procurements d 2 16
p1 Foundation reinforcement e2
p2 Slab reinforcement
p3 Precast roof units
p4 Bricks & windows

figure 4.43

YEAR 1980

CRITICAL PATH SCHEDULING CALENDAR

PROJECT SINGLE STOREY STORE
CLIENT A & B SUPPLIES
PROJECT START DATE 19th JANUARY 1980   PROJECT TARGET DATE 31st MAY 1980

	1	2	3	4	5	6	7	8	9	10	11	12	13	14	15	16	17	18	19	20	21	22	23	24	25	26	27	28	29	30	31
JANUARY	1	2	3	4	5	6	7	8	9	10	11	12	13	14	15	16	17	18	19	20	21	22	23	24	25	26	27	28	29	30	31
WORK DAY NO.	-	-	-	-	-	-	-	-	-	1	2	3	-	-	4	5	6	7	8	-	-	9	10	11	12	13	-	-	14	15	16
FEBRUARY	1	2	3	4	5	6	7	8	9	10	11	12	13	14	15	16	17	18	19	20	21	22	23	24	25	26	27	28	29		
WORK DAY NO.	17	18	-	-	19	20	21	22	23	-	-	24	25	26	27	28	-	-	29	30	31	32	33	-	-	34	35	36	37		
MARCH	1	2	3	4	5	6	7	8	9	10	11	12	13	14	15	16	17	18	19	20	21	22	23	24	25	26	27	28	29	30	31
WORK DAY NO.	38	-	-	39	40	41	42	43	-	-	44	45	46	47	48	-	-	49	50	51	52	53	-	-	54	55	56	57	58	-	-
APRIL	1	2	3	4	5	6	7	8	9	10	11	12	13	14	15	16	17	18	19	20	21	22	23	24	25	26	27	28	29	30	
WORK DAY NO.	59	60	61	62	63	-	-	64	65	66	67	68	-	-	69	70	71	72	73	-	-	74	75	76	77	78	-	-	79	-	
MAY	1	2	3	4	5	6	7	8	9	10	11	12	13	14	15	16	17	18	19	20	21	22	23	24	25	26	27	28	29	30	31
WORK DAY NO.	80	81	82	83	-	-	84	85	86	87	88	-	-	89	90	91	92	93	-	-	94	95	96	97	98	-	-	99	100	101	102
JUNE	1	2	3	4	5	6	7	8	9	10	11	12	13	14	15	16	17	18	19	20	21	22	23	24	25	26	27	28	29	30	
WORK DAY NO.	103	-	-	104	105	106	107	108	-	-	109	110	111	112	113	-	-	114	115	116	117	118	-	-	119	120	121	122	123	-	

Figure 4.44

PR	Clear site	2 days
P1	Procure foundation reinforcement	4 days
P2	Procure slab reinforcement	10 days
P3	Procure precast roof units	30 days
P4	Procure facing bricks and metal windows	35 days

4.9.2 Analysis of the Precedence Network

The analysis of the precedence network in Figure 4.42 indicates an overall project time of 102 days, the critical activities in the sequence being E1, E2, F1, F2, F3, B1, I1 and I6.   Activity E2 is only critical with regard to its earliest start date as this directly affects the commencement of the reinforced concrete columns and beams.

The precedence network has been presented in bar chart format in Figure 4.43 for utilisation at site management level.   This allows progress to be more readily recorded at site level and is a more readily acceptable form of presentation for the architect to understand.   Figure 4.44 indicates a critical path scheduling calendar which allows the day numbers to be calendar related. The key dates may be indicated on the precedence diagram by using specified date symbols.

Many construction companies give site management and surveying staff short in-company training courses on the principles and application of precedence networks.   This enables all levels of management to have an understanding of the planning system used by the company.   It also allows surveying staff to highlight the effect of delays resulting from the receipt of architects' information when formulating claims.

4.10 COST ENVELOPES - PRINCIPLES

By preparing a contract budget based on the earliest and latest start dates abstracted from a network diagram, a cost envelope may be produced.

A cost envelope is a graphical display of the value/cost plotted to a time scale. This shows the cumulative value/cost based on the earliest and latest start dates for a particular sequence of activities.

The value/time relationship approximates the following diagrammatic forms

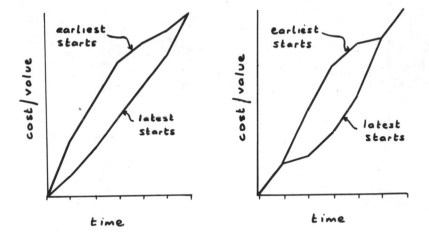

Consider the activities A, B, C, D and E as shown on the network in Figure 4.45. The network is analysed in order to establish the earliest and latest starts and the critical path. The value of each activity has also been indicated on the diagram. Analysis of the network shows that activities A and B are critical and that activities C, D and E each have 8 days float.

A calendar time scaled diagram or bar chart is shown in Figure 4.46 based on the earliest start dates for each activity (i.e. the earliest date at which each activity can be undertaken). The monetary value for each activity has been allocated to each bar line based on a linear time/value relationship and the weekly and cumulative budget totals calculated.

185

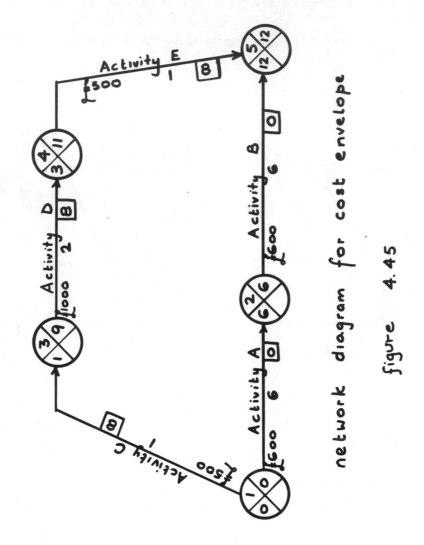

network diagram for cost envelope

figure 4.45

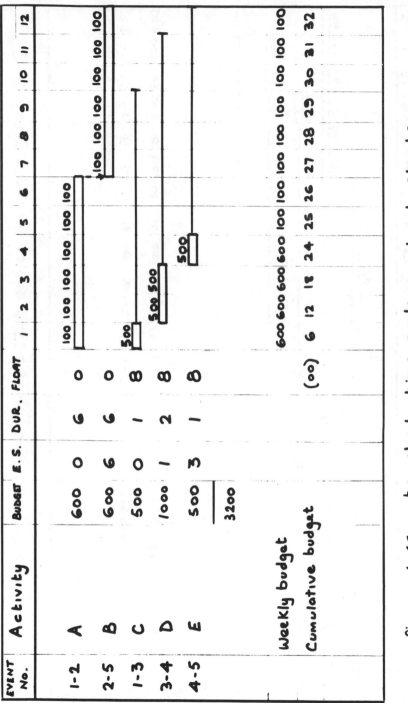

figure 4.4G   bar chart – time scale – earliest starts

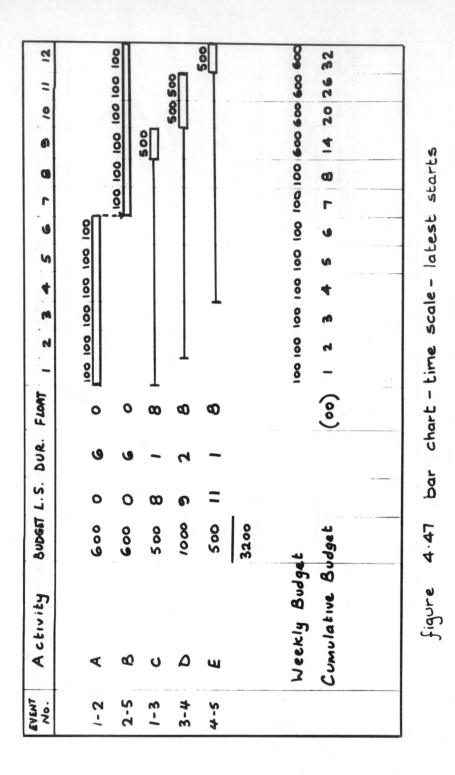

figure 4.47 bar chart – time scale – latest starts

188

Figure 4.47 shows a further bar chart indicating the latest start dates for each activity (i.e. the latest date by which each activity must be started in order that no delays occur in the overall sequence). The monetary budget has again been calculated by allocating values to the appropriate durations.

The cumulative totals for the earliest and latest starts have been plotted to a value/time scale as shown on Figure 4.48 to form the cost envelope diagram. With the earliest start situation the monetary value will be released earlier in the contract period. The plotting of the value of the latest starts indicates that the monies will be released at later dates during the contract.

During the progress of the contract the actual dates at which each activity is carried out will be recorded and the actual value released allocated accordingly. From this data the actual value/time curve for the contract can be developed and plotted on the cost envelope.

The objective of producing a cost envelope is to utilise it as a management control aid for the contractor. The actual value, or cost/time curve, should fall within the cost envelope produced. As an alternative to plotting the value, the activity cost may be plotted. In this way actual costs can be matched with the budgeted costs on the cost envelope diagram.

Figure 4.49 indicates the contract's progress recorded up to the end of week 6 and the cumulative value released to that date has been plotted on the cost envelope in Figure 4.48.

4.11 COST ENVELOPE - WORKED EXAMPLE

A network diagram for a factory project is shown in Figure 4.50. The arrow diagram has been analysed and indicates an overall contract period of 23 weeks. The forecast cost of each activity is also indicated on the network. Floats have been calculated and the critical path has been established.

Figure 4.51 indicates the bar chart produced from the network showing the relationship between earliest starts. Floats have been indicated in decreasing order on the bar chart sequence. Forecast costs have been allocated to each of the bar lines and the weekly and cumulative cost budget developed to form a summary along the bottom of the programme.

Figure 4.52 shows the bar chart based on the latest starts together with a summary of the cumulative cost budget.

Figure 4.53 indicates the cost envelope for the project based on the cost/time budget prepared for the earliest and latest starts.

During the progress of work on site the actual costs will be recorded and the cumulative actual cost/time plotted on the envelope diagram.

189

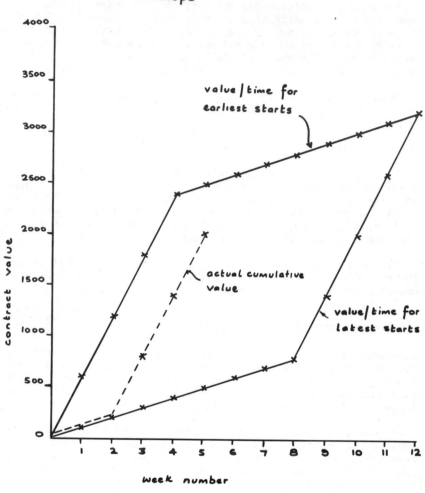

Cost Envelope

Cost envelope based on network diagram
in figure 4·45

figure 4·48

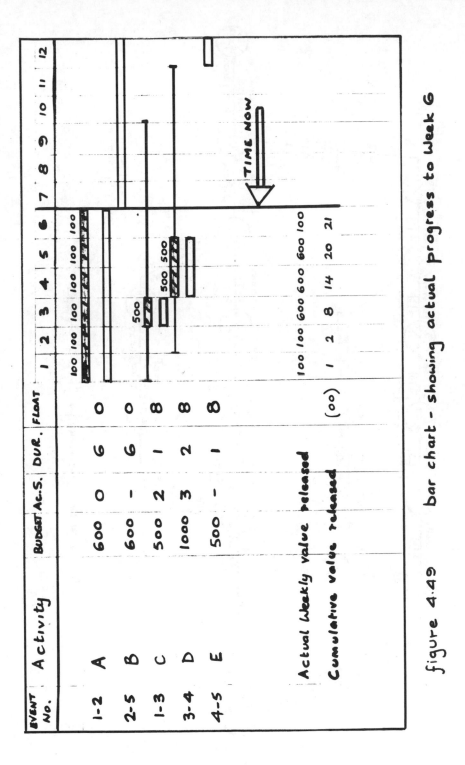

figure 4.49   bar chart - showing actual progress to Week 6

191

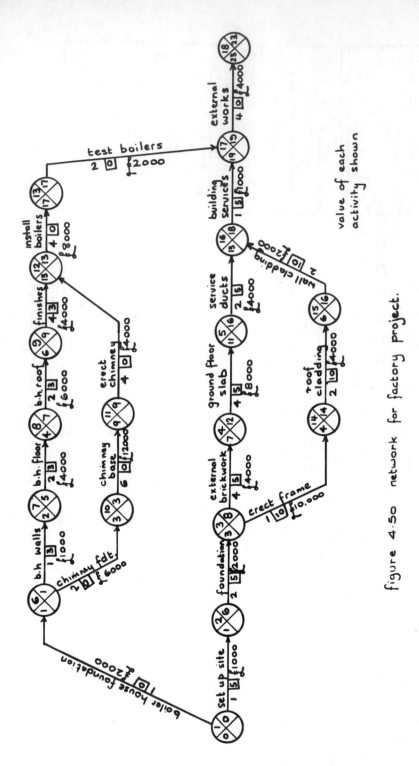

figure 4.50 network for factory project.

value of each
activity shown

figure 4.51 Factory Project- Bar chart showing latest starts.

EV. No.	Activity	E.S.	DUR.	FL.	Cost/value budget
1-6	Boiler House Fdts	0	1	0	2000
6-10	Chimney Fdts	1	2	0	6000
10-11	Chimney base	3	6	0	12000
11-12	Erect chimney	9	4	0	4000
12-13	Install boilers	13	4	0	8000
13-17	Test boilers	17	2	0	2000
17-18	External works	19	4	0	4000
6-7	Boiler House walls	1	1	3	1000
7-8	Boiler House floor	2	2	3	4000
8-9	Boiler House roof	4	2	3	2000
9-12	Boiler House finishes	6	4	3	4000
1-2	Set up site	0	1	5	1000
2-3	Foundations	1	2	5	2000
3-4	External brickwork	3	4	5	4000
4-5	Ground floor slab	7	4	6	8000
5-10	Service ducts	11	2	5	4000
16-17	Building Services	13	1	5	1000
3-14	Erect steel frame	3	1	10	10000
14-15	Roof cladding	4	2	10	4000
15-16	Wall cladding	6	2	10	2000
					85000 TOTAL budget

Completion date

Weekly budget	3	5	6	15	6	6	6	6	5	5	4	3	3	3	2	2	2	2	1	1	1	1	1	
Cumulative budget	3	8	14	29	35	41	46	52	57	61	64	67	70	73	75	77	79	80	81	82	83	84	85	
Week Number	1	2	3	4	5	6	7	8	9	10	11	12	13	14	15	16	17	18	19	20	21	22	23	24

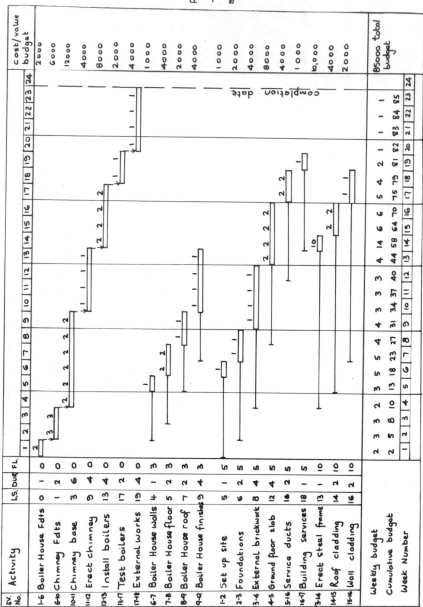

figure 4.52

Factory Project
- Bar chart
showing latest
starts

194

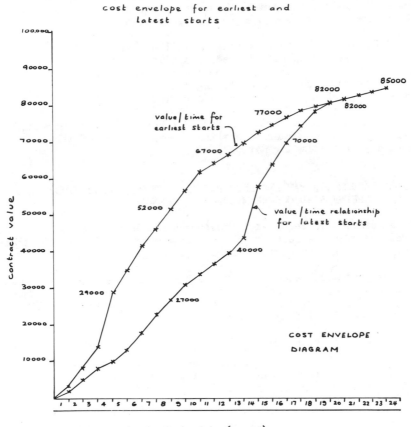

cost envelope for earliest and
latest starts

COST ENVELOPE
DIAGRAM

Contract value

value/time for
earliest starts

value/time relationship
for latest starts

100,000

90000

80000

70000

60000

50000

40000

30000

20000

10000

85000

82000

82000

77000

70000

67000

52000

40000

29000

27000

1 2 3 4 5 6 7 8 9 10 11 12 13 14 15 16 17 18 19 20 21 22 23 24

contract duration (weeks)

figure 4·53

4.12 LADDER DIAGRAMS AND LABOUR RESOURCE ALLOCATION

A ladder diagram for a network may be used for depicting repetitive sequences for a construction project. This may be applied to a housing, modernisation project or a repetitive sequence on a reinforced concrete frame.

The ladder diagram sequence may be shown in trade or gang sequence or related to the operations on each block. Figure 4.54 shows the ladder diagram block or unit orientated whereas Figure 4.55 shows the sequence gang or trade related.

Analysis of the network diagram will enable the floats and the critical path to be established. A time scaled diagram (or bar chart) may then be produced from the network in order to consider labour resources. By considering the use of float times the most economical labour balance may be achieved.

A worked example for a reinforced concrete column sequence has been developed in order to outline the principles of labour resourcing from a ladder network.

4.13 LADDER DIAGRAM AND RESOURCE ALLOCATION - CASE STUDY - REINFORCED CONCRETE COLUMN SEQUENCE

An assessment is required of the optimum labour resources for the erection of three rows of columns for a reinforced concrete framed building. A plan of the column layout is shown in Figure 4.56.

The programme sequence is to be based on using 3 sets of column shutters, i.e. one complete set for each row of columns. The sequence of erection is to be repeated on 8 floors of a multistorey framed building.

Three gangs of operatives are to be used, each made up as follows

2   - Steel fixers fabricating and fixing reinforcement
4   - Carpenters fixing column formwork
4   - Labourers for the concreting operations
4   - Carpenters striking formwork

The following durations have been allocated to each operation

	Duration per row of columns
Fabricate and fix reinforcement to columns	1 day
Fix formwork to columns	2 days
Concrete columns	1 day
Strike formwork to columns	1 day

The objective of the case study is to establish the most economic utilisation of labour resources.

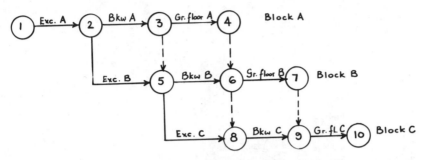

figure 4.54 Ladder diagram in Block sequence

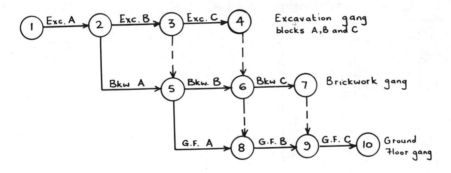

figure 4.55 Ladder diagram in Trade or Gang sequence

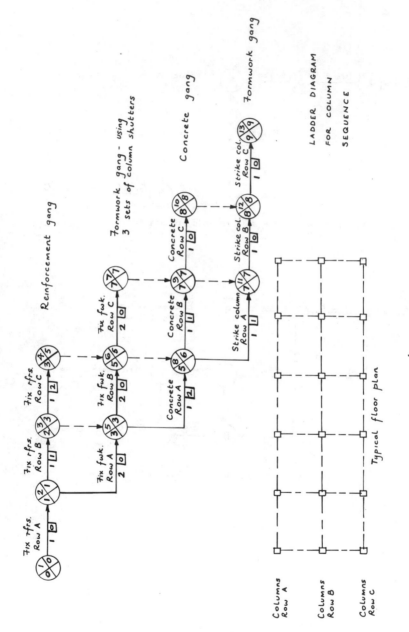

Fix rfrs. Row A

Fix rfrs. Row B

Fix rfrs. Row C

Fix fwk. Row A

Fix fwk. Row B

Fix fwk. Row C

Concrete Row A

Concrete Row B

Concrete Row C

Strike column Row A

Strike col. Row B

Strike col. Row C

Reinforcement gang

Formwork gang – using 3 sets of column shutters

Concrete gang

Formwork gang

LADDER DIAGRAM
FOR COLUMN
SEQUENCE

Columns Row A

Columns Row B

Columns Row C

Typical floor plan

figure 4.56

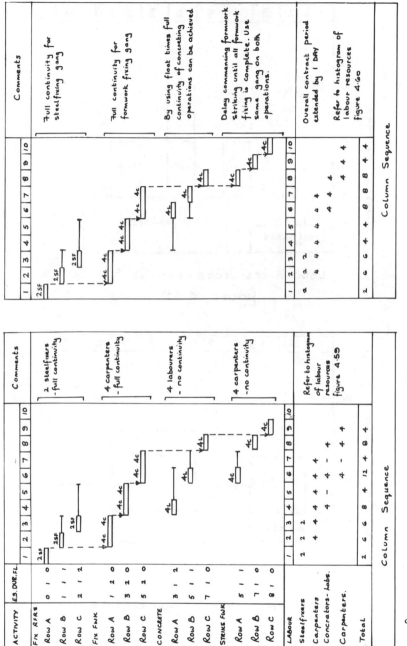

Figure 4·57 Earliest Start - Bar chart Presentation

Figure 4·58 Optimum solution for labour utilisation

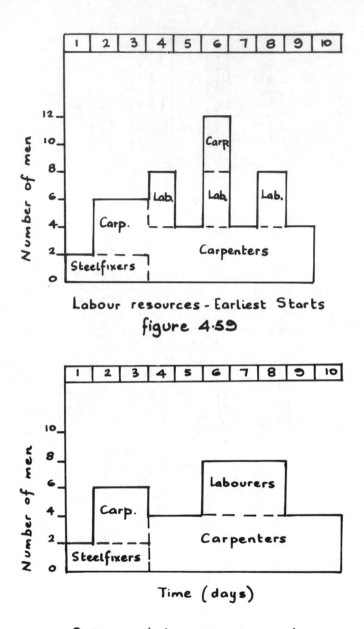

Labour resources - Earliest Starts
figure 4·59

Time (days)

Optimum Labour requirements

Resource Analysis for Column Sequence
figure 4·60

A ladder network diagram for the column sequence is shown in Figure 4.56. The sequence of activities has been trade or gang orientated in order to group together the various trade gangs on the bar chart showing earliest starts. The critical path and floats for each activity have been established on the network diagram.

The critical trade sequence can be observed to be the fixing of column formwork and its subsequent striking activity. The overall duration for the column sequence for one floor has been established as 9 days.

A bar chart indicating the earliest starts is shown in Figure 4.57 and the labour gangs allocated to each activity have been added to the bar lines.

A summary of the labour requirements is shown under the bar chart and the labour totals have been represented in the form of a histogram in Figure 4.59. The labour resources can be seen to vary widely throughout the sequence due to non-continuity of concreting operations and a one day delay in the formwork striking.

Alternative considerations to enable continuity of work for each trade gang are shown in Figure 4.58. By using the float times on the concreting sequence for the columns, continuity of work for the concrete gang can be obtained.

By delaying the striking of the column formwork until completion of the fixing of the columns, gang continuity for the carpenters can also be attained.

The alternative labour assessment is shown on the bar chart in Figure 4.58 and this is represented as a labour resource histogram in Figure 4.60.

The analysis indicates that by extending the programme cycle by 1 day (i.e. from 9 days to 10 days) continuity of work can be achieved for the various trade gangs.

4.14 TIME COST OPTIMISATION TECHNIQUES AND LEAST COST SCHEDULING

Principles

This technique is based on the principle of reducing the overall time on a network diagram by considering alternative durations (crash times). Refer to 4.7 – Network Analysis – Crash Cost Application.

The average cost involved in reducing an activity's duration by one unit in time (one day or one week, whichever is applicable) is termed the cost slope. The cost slope is assumed to be a linear relationship and may be calculated as follows

$$\text{Cost slope} = \frac{\text{Crash cost} - \text{Normal cost}}{\text{Normal time} - \text{Crash time}}$$

i.e. $$\text{Cost slope} = \frac{\text{Increase in cost}}{\text{Reduction in time}} = \text{cost/day}$$

If an activity has a normal time of 10 days and a normal cost of £1000, and a crash time of 8 days and a crash cost of £1300 - the cost slope will be

$$\text{Cost slope} = \frac{£1300 - £1000}{10d - 8d} = \frac{£300}{2d} = £150/\text{day}$$

The average cost of reducing the duration of the activity by one day is £150. This is termed the cost slope.

Least cost scheduling is the process of finding the least cost situation for an overall project. It is based on reducing the duration of activities on the critical path by considering the rank order of their cost slopes. The process is repeated for each activity until the least cost situation is achieved.

Complications occur however when, by changing durations, the critical path may change. This will affect floats on non-critical activities and thus affect the decision to use crash times or normal times on these activities. In certain circumstances it may involve a re-appraisal of the complete network in order to assess the least cost situation.

4.15 TIME COST OPTIMISATION EXAMPLE
PROJECT INFORMATION

Figure 4.61 shows a network for part of a project. The latest progress report indicates that due to delivery problems the earliest starting time for operations 12-13 and 12-14 will be day 51. The master programme indicates that operation 19-20 must be completed no later than day 81 so as not to delay the remainder of the project.

Data relating to the cost slopes for activities 14-16 and 16-19 are shown and these have been calculated and inserted on the Figure 4.61.

	Activity - event numbers	
	14-16	16-19
Normal duration	10 days	6 days
Normal cost	£520	£300
Crash duration/time	8 days	4 days
Crash cost	£570	£352

A report is to be prepared for senior management in order to advise them of the cost implications of completing operation 19-20 on or before day 81.

Network Diagram — Analysed using Normal Times

Floats based on using normal times

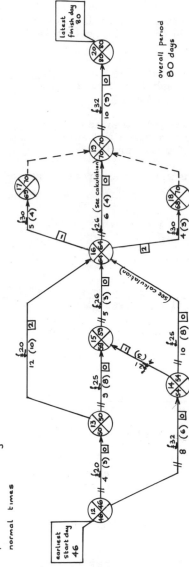

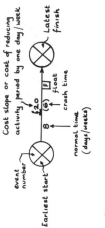

Critical Path (12-13, 13-15, 15-16, 16-15, 19-20) and path (12-14, 14-16, 16-19, 19-20)

overall period 80 days

Key to Network

figure 4.61

4.16 APPROACH TO THE ANALYSIS OF THE PROBLEM

The problem is to be analysed by considering the following stages in order to formulate a conclusion.

Stage 1 - Calculation of cost slopes for activity 14-16, 16-19.

Stage 2 - Analysis of the initial network diagram shown in Figure 4.61 using normal durations in order to establish the critical path.

Stage 3 - Consideration to complete the project earlier than day 81 by considering crash durations and the calculation of the least cost situation.

Stage 4 - Consideration to complete the project on day 81 by using normal times and crash times and establishing the least cost optimisation for the project.

Stage 5 - Formulating conclusions for a report to senior management.

4.17 PROBLEM ANALYSIS - STAGE 1
CALCULATION OF COST SLOPES

Operation/activity 14-16

$$\text{Cost slope} = \frac{\text{Crash cost} - \text{Normal cost}}{\text{Normal time} - \text{Crash time}} = \frac{£570 - £520}{10 - 8}$$

$$= \frac{£50}{2} = £25/\text{day} - \text{cost slope}$$

Operation/activity 16-19

$$= \frac{£352 - £300}{6 - 4} = \frac{£52}{2}$$

$$= £26/\text{day} - \text{cost slope}$$

i.e. the cost slope of operation 14-16 is £25/day, the cost slope of operation 16-19 is £26/day - [the average increase in cost for reducing the operations duration by 1 unit of time, i.e. 1 day].

4.18 STAGE 2 - ANALYSIS OF INITIAL NETWORK DIAGRAM -
USING NORMAL TIMES

The analysis of Figure 4.61 indicates that the initial project, commencing at day 46, will be completed on day 80.

The critical path for the network diagram follows the activities 12-13, 13-15, 15-16, 16-19, and 19-20. A further critical path follows activities 12-14, 14-16, 16-19, and 19-20.   Two critical

Network Diagram - Analysed using Crash Times

floats based on using all
crash times

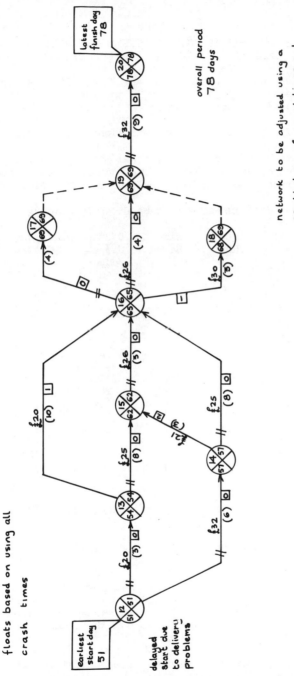

figure 4.62

network to be adjusted using a
combination of normal times and
crash times to finish on Day 81

paths are evident due to the loop 12-14-16 having the same duration as loop 12-13-15 and 16, i.e. 18 days.

4.19 STAGE 3 - ANALYSIS TO COMPLETE THE (PROGRAMME) PROJECT EARLIER THAN DAY 81 USING ALL CRASH TIMES

The analysis is shown in Figure 4.62 and this indicates a project commencement date of day 51 in order to incorporate the revised delivery programme for the project.

The latest finish date has been established as day 78.

Using the crash durations the critical path is as previously established plus operation 16-17. The additional cost incurred in using all crash times can be calculated in the following way.

Least Cost Assessment using Crash Durations

Event No.	Normal Time	Crash Time	Time Saved	Cost Slope /day	Additional Cost	Floats (days)
12-13	4	3	1	20	20	0
13-15	9	8	1	25	25	0
15-16	5	3	2	26	52	0
16-19	6	4	2	26	52	0
19-20	10	9	1	32	32	0
12-14	8	6	2	32	64	0
14-16	10	8	2	25	50	0
14-15	4	3	1	21	21	1
13-16	12	10	2	20	40	2
16-17	5	4	1	30	30	2
16-18	4	3	1	30	30	1
					£416	

Total additional cost to complete the project on day 78 using all crash durations is £416.

ANALYSIS TO COMPLETE THE PROJECT ON DAY 78 USING A COMBINATION OF CRASH DURATIONS AND NORMAL DURATIONS

The most economical way to complete the project at a least cost within 78 days is to consider the rank order of the operations containing float. The rank order is determined by considering their cost slope, i.e. the operations with the lowest cost slope are higher in the ranking.

On considering Figure 4.62 we have three activities with float i.e. 13-16, 14-15 and 16-18.

Least Cost Optimisation – 78 days

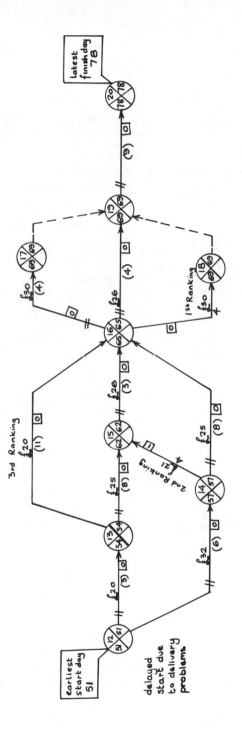

figure 4·63

LEAST COST = £345

In the least cost situation all activities
are critical with the exception of event
14-15 which has one day's float

crash time on event 13-14 has been
adjusted to 11 days

Activity	Normal time	Crash time	Float	Cost slope	Ranking
13-16	12	10	1	£20.0	1st
14-15	3	2	2	£21.0	2nd
16-18	4	3	1	£30.0	3rd

By adjusting these floats on the network diagram and still completing the project by day 78 a lower least cost situation can be obtained.

The adjusted network is shown in Figure 4.63. The floats on activity 13-16 and 16-18 have been reduced to zero whilst a 1 day float occurs on activity 14-15.

Least Cost Optimisation for 78 Days Latest Finish

Event No.	Normal Time	Crash Time	Time Saved	Cost Slope /day	Additional Cost	Floats (days)
12-13	4	3	1	20	20	0
13-15	9	8	1	25	25	0
15-16	5	3	2	26	52	0
16-19	6	4	2	26	52	0
19-20	10	9	1	32	32	0
12-14	8	6	2	32	64	0
14-16	10	8	2	25	50	0
14-15	4	4	0	21	0	1
13-16	12	11	1	20	20	0
16-17	5	4	1	30	30	0
16-18	4	4	0	30	0	0
					£345	

Least cost optimisation to complete project on day 78 is £345.

4.20 STAGE 4 - ANALYSIS TO COMPLETE THE PROJECT ON DAY 81 AND ESTABLISH THE LEAST COST

In order to complete the project by day 81 the overall time on the network diagram as shown in Figure 4.64 must be reduced by 4 days, i.e. from a latest finish of 85 days to day 81.

The most economical reduction can again be achieved by considering the rank order of the cost slopes on the critical path. This will enable 4 days to be deducted from the durations on the critical path.

The rank order is as follows

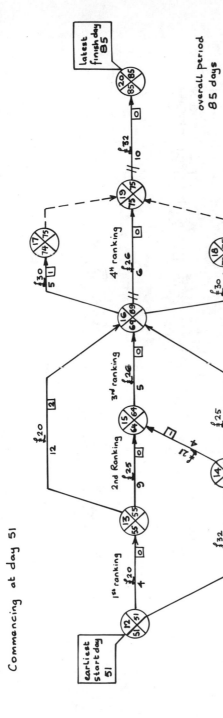

Network Diagram - Analysed using normal times

Commencing at day 51

overall period 85 days

Overall duration to be reduced by 4 days in order to complete project by day 81.

Order of ranking indicated on network. Activities on critical path 12-13, 13-15, 15-16 and 16-19.

Rank order of reductions

1st	12-13	Cost slope	£20
2nd	13-15	Cost slope	£25
3rd	15-16	Cost slope	£26
4th	16-19	Cost slope	£26

figure 4.64

209

Least Cost Optimisation - 81 days

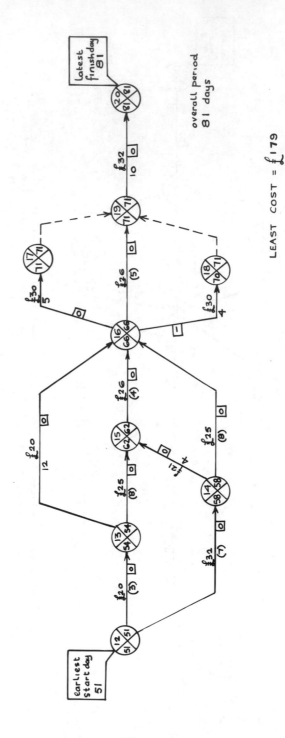

figure 4.65

LEAST COST = £179

210

Rank Order	Operation	Cost Slope	Normal Time	Crash Time	Days Saved
1st	12–13	£20	4	3	1
2nd	13–15	£25	9	8	1
3rd	15–16	£26	5	4	1
4th	16–19	£26	6	5	$\underline{1}$
					4 days

The use of the crash times will directly affect operations 12–14, 14–16 and 14–15. Operations 13–16 and 14–15 need not be considered in the ranking as they are not critical.

Figure 4.65 indicates the final network diagram and the assessment of the least cost situation is shown in tabular form.

Event No.	Normal Time	Crash Time	Time Saved	Cost Slope /day	Additional Cost	Float
12–13	4	3	1	20	20	0
13–15	9	8	1	25	25	0
15–16	5	4	1	26	26	0
16–19	6	5	1	26	26	0
19–20	10	10	0	26	0	0
12–14	8	7	1	32	32	0
14–16	10	8	2	25	50	0
14–15	4	4	0	21	0	0
13–16	12	12	0	20	0	0
16–17	5	5	0	30	0	0
16–18	4	4	0	30	$\underline{0}$	1
					£179	

Least cost optimisation for project completion on day 81 is £179.

4.21 STAGE 5 – CONCLUSIONS – REPORT TO MANAGEMENT

The most economical solution is to complete the project sequence on day 81 at a least cost of £179.

Speeding up the project to complete it by day 78 is less economical as this shows a least cost of £345.

It is recommended that the sequence of the network indicated in Figure 4.65 is adopted for the project.

NOTE

The basis of this least cost optimisation example has been taken from the Chartered Institute of Building examination 1983, Final Part II Building Production and Project Management Paper 1, Question 6.

The problem has however been extended to indicate the application of least cost scheduling when considering finishing a project earlier than planned or on a programme based on updated site planning information.

REFERENCES - CONTRACT PLANNING

1. National Building Agency, Programming House Building by Line of Balance.

2. Oxley, R. and Thompson, P.W., Critical Path Success or Failure. Institute of Building Technology and Management. February, 1980.

BIBLIOGRAPHY

Institute of Building - Site Management Information Service Papers.

No.41, November, 1971 - Site Management - A Time for Rethinking.

No.46, September, 1972 - Management Contracting.

No.51. July, 1973 - Modern Site Control Methods Suitable for the Larger Project.

No.68. Winter. 1976 - Storage on Site.

No.74 Summer, 1978 - Incentives in the Construction Industry.

No.75. Autumn, 1978 - The Control of Materials on Housing Sites.

No.76, Winter, 1978 - Planning and Organisational Problems Associated with Confined Sites.

Hollins, R.J., Production and Planning Applied to Building (George Goodwin, 1962).

Burgess, R.A. and White, G., Building Production and Project Management (Construction Press, 1979).

O'Brien, J.J., CPM in Construction Management (McGraw-Hill, 1965).

Harris, F. and McCaffer, R., Modern Construction Management (Crosby Lockwood Staples, 1977).

Calvert, R.E., Introduction to Building Management (George Newnes, 1964).

Institute of Building - Programmes in Construction .... a guide to good practice. Published January 1981

This reference provides practical guidance on the subject of programming. The importance of teamwork at both head office and site management level is emphasised together with the most effective forms of construction programmes for different circumstances. The guide states that there is no one correct way - different organisations and different projects call for different treatment.

5 SHORT TERM PLANNING PROCEDURES AND PROGRESS RECORDING

5.1 SHORT TERM CONTRACT PLANNING

Short term planning encompasses all programming and planning
procedures undertaken during the progress of work on site.
This includes the preparation of stage programmes every four to
six weeks. Stage programmes enable the master programme to be
broken down into greater detail and more manageable proportions
and takes into account current resources and information available from the architect and consulting engineer. Weekly planning
by the site foreman enables the requirements of the stage programming to be analysed into further detail and directly involves
site management decision making. This enables subcontractors
and suppliers to be closely integrated into the planning process.

5.1.1 Objectives of Short Term Planning

(1) The main objective is to keep the master programme under
     constant review in order to achieve completion of the
     project by the planned date.

(2) The reviewing process should lead to more effective site
     management ultimately affecting the utilisation of labour,
     materials and plant.

(3) To highlight information requirements in order to meet
     planned completion dates for each stage of the work.

(4) To keep senior management informed of the progress position.

5.1.2 The Five Week Stage Programme

A detailed programme usually in bar chart form should be prepared
to cover site operations to be undertaken over the succeeding
five week period. This should reflect the requirements of the
master programme and provide a realistic forward view based on
the drawings, sequence of operations and resources available.
Figures 5.1 and 5.2 illustrate the layout of a stage programme.
Figure 5.1 indicates a programme for the first five weeks of a
factory project. Figure 5.2 shows the sequence of operations
for a housing project. The programme for the following five
week period will be prepared at the end of the fourth week in
the programme thus allowing a one week reviewing and overlap
period between successive programmes. Every operation to be
undertaken must be carefully analysed and new operations added
to the programme as they are implemented. Operations behind
programmes are highlighted at each stage of the planning process
and this enables site management to determine the action to be
taken to recover lost time.

Contract Alderley   Short-term   Stage Programme —— 5 week stage   Date 5 January
Programme No. 1   to   6 February

No.	Operation	Value (£)	Man-hours	Man-days	Gang size	Gang days	w/e day / day no	9 Jan	16 Jan	23 Jan	30 Jan	6 Feb
1	Set up site	500L	200	25	3 lab. 1 carp.	6						
2	Reduced level excavation	Subcontract P.T. Moore				10						
3	External services	265L	106	13	1 lab.	13						
4	External drainage	864pl	108	13·5	J.C.B. 3c	15						
		1890L	756	94·5	4 lab 3 bl	13						
5	Internal drainage	500pl	62·5	8	J.C.B. 3c	8						
		979L	392	49	4 lab.	12						
6	Stanchion base excavation	264pl	33	4	J.C.B. 3c	4						
		950L	380	47·5	3 lab.	16						
7	Concrete bases	1050pl	131	16·5	J.C.B. 3c	16						
		300L	120	15	3 lab.	5						
8	Hardcore slab	320L	128	16	2 lab.	8						
		480pl	48	6	btd100	6						

Concrete by excavation gang

Prepare next 5 week programme

Gang schedule
Labourers   3 3 3 3   4 4 4 4 4   7 7 7   11 11 11 11   7 7 7   9 9 9 9 9
Carpenters   1 1 1 1
Bricklayers   3 3 3 3 3   3 3 3   3 3 3 3 3   3 3 3   3 3 3 3 3

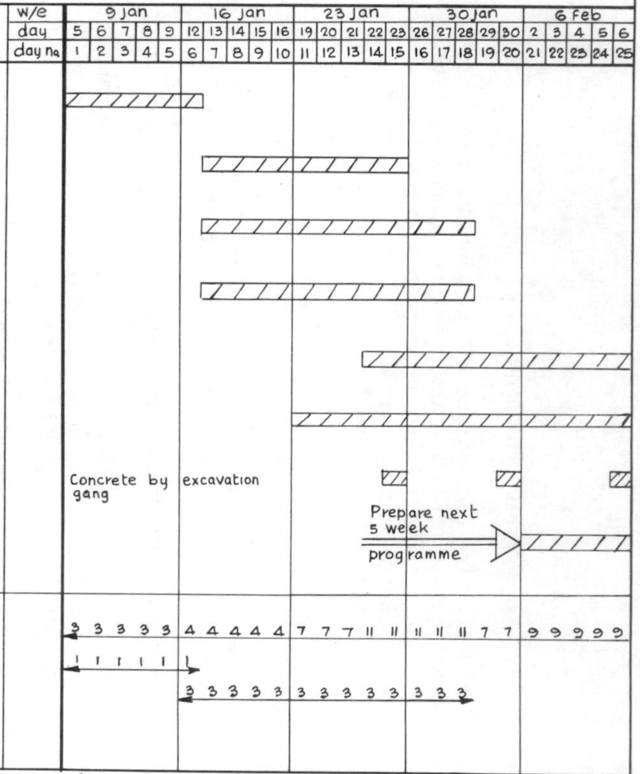

Figure 5.1

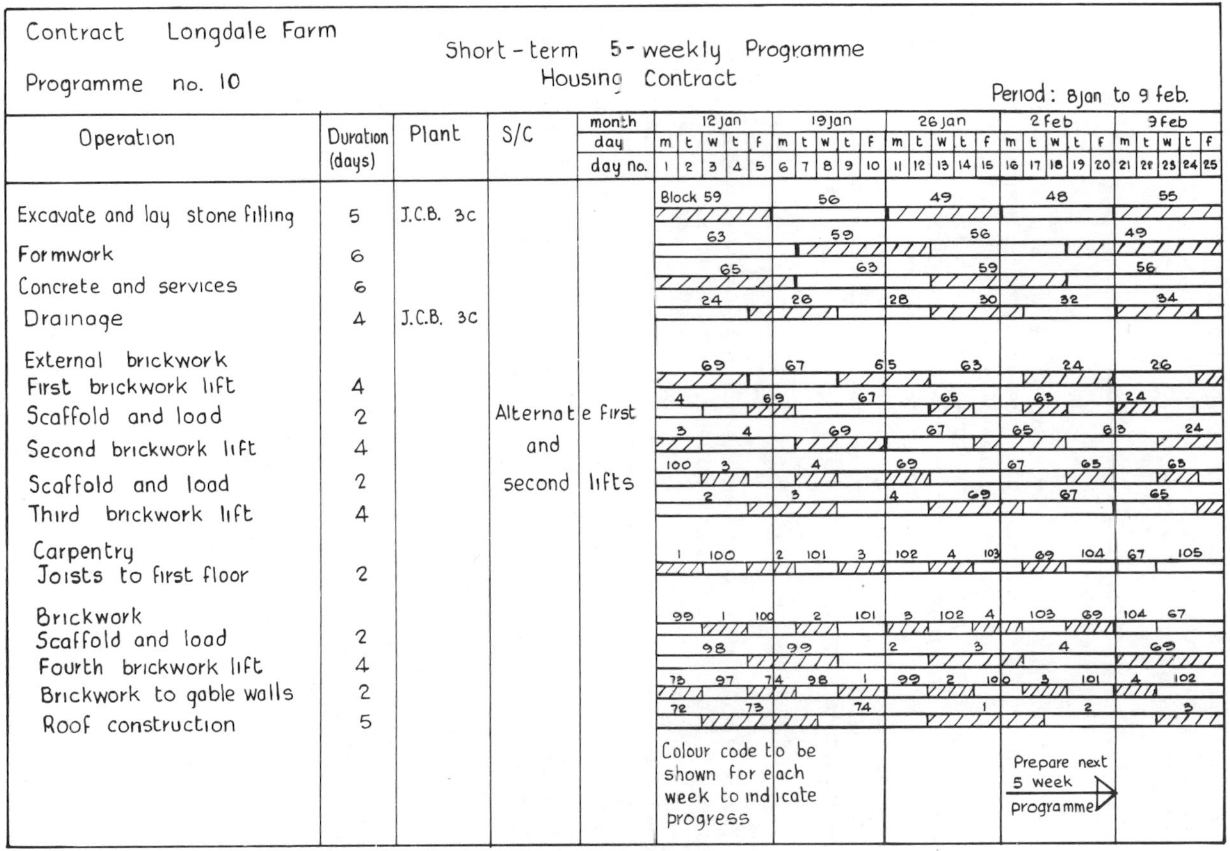

Contract   Longdale Farm   Short-term 5-weekly Programme

Programme   no. 10   Housing Contract   Period: 8 Jan to 9 Feb.

Operation	Duration (days)	Plant	S/C
Excavate and lay stone filling	5	J.C.B. 3c	
Formwork	6		
Concrete and services	6	J.C.B. 3c	
Drainage	4	J.C.B. 3c	
External brickwork / First brickwork lift	4		Alternate first
Scaffold and load	2		and
Second brickwork lift	4		second lifts
Scaffold and load	2		
Third brickwork lift	4		
Carpentry / Joists to first floor	2		
Brickwork	2		
Scaffold and load	4		
Fourth brickwork lift	2		
Brickwork to gable walls	5		
Roof construction			

Calendar columns — month: 12 jan | 19 jan | 26 jan | 2 feb | 9 feb; day: m t w t f (repeated each week); day no.: 1–25.

Colour code to be shown for each week to indicate progress

Prepare next 5 week programme

Figure 5.2

215

The duration of each operation may be derived from an analysis of man-hour allocations or simply be based on the experience of the site manager and planning engineer. An example of the assessment of operational times are shown in Figure 5.3 on the programme calculation sheet. Subcontract operations may be integrated into the stage programming or a separate subcontractor's programme prepared as shown in Figure 5.4.

5.1.3 The Relationship Between Short Term Planning and Monthly Site Meetings

It is common practice to review the contract's progress at monthly time intervals to coincide with the architect's monthly site meeting. At this point in time it is opportune to hold co-ordination meetings with subcontractors' representatives to discuss key dates, information requirements and the integration of subcontractors' work into the short term programme. A programme for subcontractors' work is illustrated in Figure 5.4. Meetings with subcontractors may also be arranged to coincide with the architect's monthly site meeting.

5.1.4 Updating the Stage Programme

Progress will be recorded on the bar chart at the end of each week by the site planning engineer, production control or the site manager. Methods of progress recording are illustrated in Section 5.4.4. The progress recording highlights operations either behind or ahead of schedule. This indicates to the site manager critical operations which require attention in the immediate short term period. Where a contract has fallen behind schedule, the stage programme clearly indicates to the architect, the contractor's intention to improve the progress position.

Once a contract has fallen behind programme due to delays created by either the main contractor, subcontractors or architect, it is not always possible to recover the delay period. Doubling the number of operatives may not necessarily reduce the operational time by fifty percent. Short term planning procedures assist in controlling work in the immediate future and enables the contractor to review his resources in the light of the job progress position.

5.1.5 Considerations when Preparing a Short Term Programme

(1) Continuity of work between gangs must be considered. On a housing development bricklaying gangs may work on alternate blocks, being moved in sequence between blocks or lifts of brickwork in conjunction with scaffolding gangs. Joinery gangs may be alternated between first, second and final fixing work and labouring gangs may be linked with concreting, services and hardcoring operations. On the one-off type project an optimum gang size must be determined for, say concreting operations, and the gang economically deployed on a variety of tasks between concreting operations.

Programme Calculation Sheet

Notes	Operation	Labour				Plant			
		Total man-hours	Gang size	Gang hours	Gang days	Machine-hours	Machine days	Machine weeks	Plant item
	Excavate oversite	–	–	–	–	88	11	2	BTD 100
	Excavate Foundations	108	1 lab.	108	14	144	18	3·5	JCB 3c
	Concrete Foundations	100	2 lab.	50	6	R.M.C. supply, direct discharge			
	External drainage	740	2 lab.	370	to	340	42·5	8·5	JCB 3c
		Drainage gang to concrete foundations as required							
	Brickwork	320	2 b/l 1 lab.	160	20	–	–	–	–
	Service connections	140	2 lab.	70	9	–	–	–	–
	Hardcore to slab	160	2 lab.	80	10	102	13	2·5	BTD 100

Notes

Durations are assessed from the man-hour allocation abstracted from the estimate or based on the quantity of work times the target rate:

rate × quantity = man-hours

$$\frac{\text{man-hours}}{\text{gang size}} = \text{gang-hours}$$

$$\frac{\text{gang-hours}}{\text{hours/day}} = \text{gang-days}$$

$$\frac{\text{gang-days}}{\text{days/week}} = \text{gang-weeks}$$

Master programme in weeks, short-term planning in days.

Figure 5.3

217

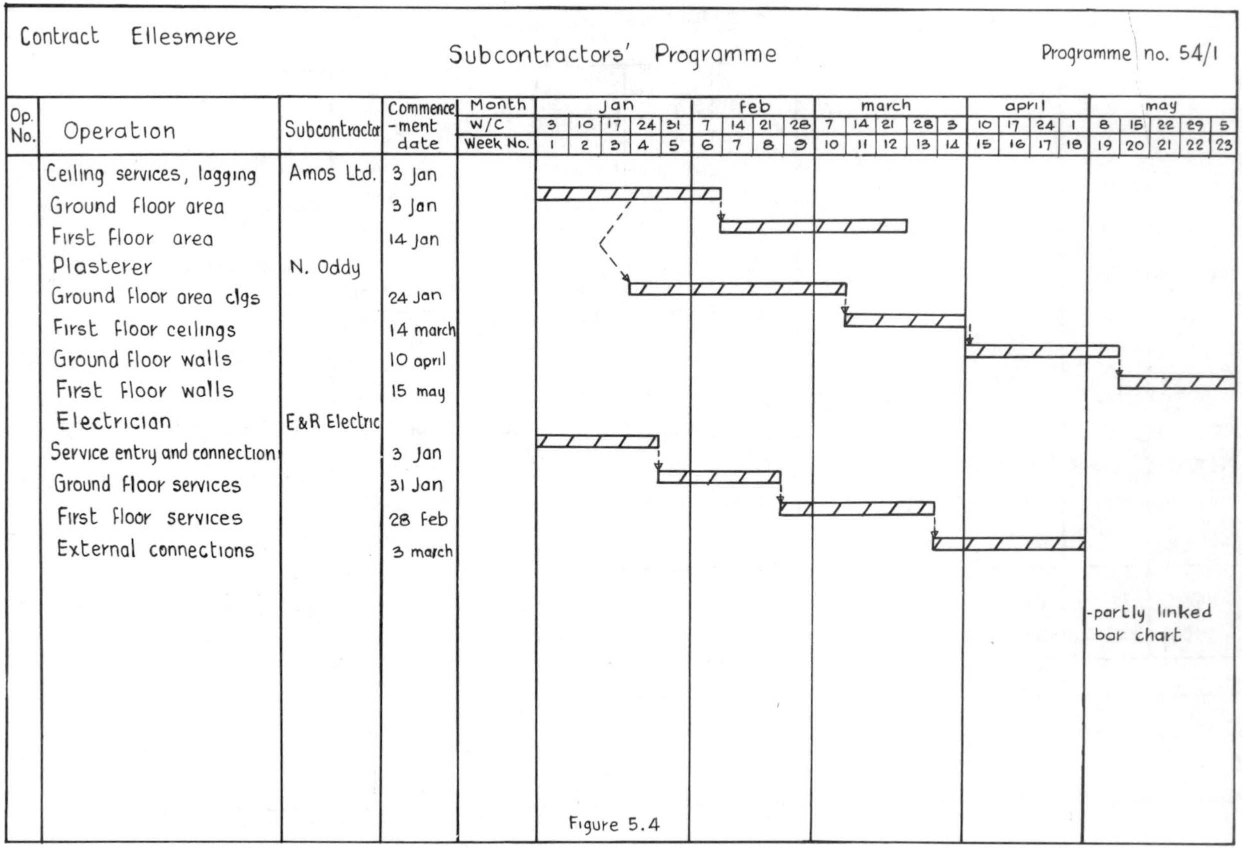

Contract Ellesmere — Subcontractors' Programme — Programme no. 54/1

Op. No.	Operation	Subcontractor	Commencement date	Month W/C Week No.	Jan				Feb				march				april				may		
					3	10 17 24 31			7 14 21 28				7 14 21 28				10 17 24 1				8 15 22 29 5		
					1 2 3 4 5				6 7 8 9				10 11 12 13 14				15 16 17 18 19				20 21 22 23		
	Ceiling services, lagging	Amos Ltd.	3 Jan																				
	Ground Floor area		3 Jan																				
	First Floor area		14 Jan																				
	Plasterer	N. Oddy																					
	Ground Floor area clgs		24 Jan																				
	First Floor ceilings		14 march																				
	Ground Floor walls		10 april																				
	First Floor walls		15 may																				
	Electrician	E&R Electric																					
	Service entry and connection		3 Jan																				
	Ground Floor services		31 Jan																				
	First Floor services		28 Feb																				
	External connections		3 march																				

— partly linked bar chart

Figure 5.4

218

(2) Subcontract work should be arranged to be completed in the least number of visits to site as possible. This may involve planning a number of house units to be brought to a similar stage prior to calling the subcontractor to site. This may be applied to roof tiling, services and painting trades. Illustrations on continuity of work for various trade gangs are shown in Figures 4.9, 4.10 and 4.11.

(3) The continuous employment of plant may be achieved by the careful planning of related plant operations. Excavation plant may be moved from site stripping to the reduced level excavation and hardcoring of roads. Multipurpose excavation plant may be alternated between foundation trench excavation and drainage work in order to provide continuity.

(4) The overlap between related operations must be considered. On a steel-framed building project an overlap of operations will occur between operations such as reduced level excavation, foundation bases, frame erection and roof sheeting operations. A clear understanding of the construction process based on experience is required in order to establish the relationship between operations.

It may prove advantageous for prospective site management personnel to receive instruction in basic planning techniques relating to company policy in the form of company planning courses or seminars. Site management certificate and diploma courses have been developed on a modular basis by the Chartered Institute of Building for site management personnel. Such courses embody planning principles and enable the site manager to participate in a variety of planning techniques during the course of study.

5.2 MONTHLY SITE MEETINGS

In order to co-ordinate requirements and review progress, regular site meetings should be arranged. The meetings should be attended by the main contractor and his principal subcontractors, any professional consultants employed by the client, the architect and clerk of works. Meetings should be conducted in a formal manner in accordance with good committee practice with an agenda sent out beforehand and minutes circulated preferably not later than one week after the meeting has taken place.

Agreement should first be reached between the architect and contractor as to the responsibility for chairing the site meetings together with the format of the agenda. Well organised site meetings will do a great deal towards providing a new impetus to the job by enabling re-organisation where delays or difficulties have affected the programme. They help to avoid delays by the careful planning of future operations and by open discussion with the parties involved. Site meetings assist in resolving difficulties before they generate friction and lead to misunderstanding between the various parties.

5.2.1 The Site Meeting Agenda

This enables the meeting to follow an organised pattern each month
and assists in recording factually the points discussed.   Agenda
numbers should be prefixed by the site meeting number in order to
assist in tracing references through the minutes of previous site
meetings.   The agenda should include the following

Item No.   Agenda

1.1   Record of personnel attending

1.2   Confirmation of minutes of previous meeting

1.3   Matters arising from previous minutes

1.4   Confirmation of matters raised at intermediate site
        visits by the architect

1.5   Progress review.   Report on progress position, plan
        of future action proposed by contractor.   Report
        from clerk of works

1.6   Drawings and information requirements

1.7   Queries relating to construction, materials or design

1.8   Forward planning - anticipated future requirements
        and outstanding problems.   Subcontractors problem
        areas.

1.9   Variation orders - confirmation of instructions

1.10   Financial review - quantity surveying matters

1.11   Any other business

1.12   Date and time of next meeting

An action column must be included on the site minutes so that
there is no confusion as to who is responsible for dealing with
the items minuted.   A minutes clerk may attend the meeting in
order to record accurately the points raised by the various
parties, alternatively the minutes will be recorded by the chairman of the meeting.   Within certain organisations a subcontractor's
site meeting will be held immediately prior to the architect's
meeting.   This enables the phasing-in of subcontractors' work to
be discussed and problem areas highlighted for discussion with the
architect at the monthly meeting.   An agenda for a first site
meeting is indicated in The Architect in Practice by A.J. Willis
and W.N.B. George (Granada).

5.3 WEEKLY PLANNING TECHNIQUES

Weekly site planning procedures used by contractors vary widely
between firms.   The majority of the small and medium-sized firms
simply leave the day to day organisation on site to the construction manager.   Many projects are managed by the crisis method of
management, e.g. they move from one crisis to another each week.
Other firms relate the weekly planning to the requirements of the
monthly or stage programme by undertaking detailed planning each
week.

5.3.1 The Weekly Plan of Work

The weekly planning procedures outlined involve the co-ordination
of trades foreman, subcontractors' representatives, site planning
engineer and the construction manager.

A weekly site meeting will be held on the Friday morning of
each week with the personnel indicated above in order to discuss
the programme of work for the following week.   This will involve
reviewing the requirements of the stage programme and the previous
week's weekly plan of work.   The work to be undertaken by each
trade gang will be assessed in joint consultation with the various
foremen and construction manager.   The work will then be inter-
preted into a workable plan of work by the planning engineer.
Subcontractors' work for the weekly period may be assessed on a
separate plan of work sheet.

An illustration of the weekly plan of work is illustrated in
Figures 5.5 and 5.6.

The involvement of the trades foreman is an important part of
the weekly planning process as it directly involves them in
decision making.   It enables the construction site manager to
co-ordinate the trades and highlights any problem areas relating
to labour and plant resources.

On finalising the weekly plan of work, copies should be distributed to the site manager, planning engineer, head office and the
participating trades foreman.   As an alternative, target tear-off
strips for individual gangs may be distributed to each gang foreman.
Progress during the week must be monitored at the end of each day
by crossing through the operations which have been completed.
Operations behind programme are thus immediately highlighted and
become a priority for the following day.

The weekly plan of work may form the basis of the weekly cost
control procedures as outlined in Section 5.5.   By introducing
an incentive in the form of a planned bonus for achieving the
programme of work, operatives may be sufficiently motivated to
make the system a workable success.

221

Weekly Plan of Work

Contract _____ Week commencing _____

Week no. _____

Trade	Labour	Plant	Monday	Tuesday	Wednesday	Thursday	Friday	Delay and Action
								Monday
								Tuesday
								Wednesday
								Thursday
								Friday

Figure 5.5

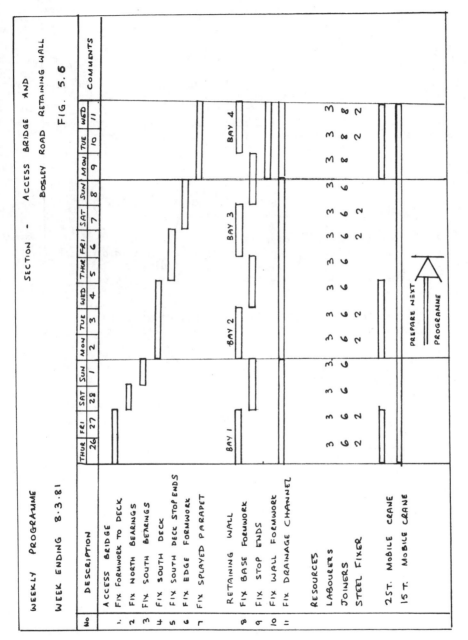

Figure 5.6

Daily work schedules for each gang may be issued by the general foreman relating to individual tasks for gangs engaged on a variety of operations in the same day.   Work schedules may also be prepared to co-ordinate the utilisation of tower cranes and fork-lift trucks between gangs.

5.4   WEEKLY SITE REPORTS AND PROGRESS RECORDING

An important part of the site manager's responsibility is the keeping of site records and the submission to the contractor's head office of weekly reports.   The contracts director or contracts manager is responsibly for analysing the weekly information received and implementing the appropriate action in order to provide assistance to the site manager.

5.4.1   Objectives of Weekly Reports

(1)   To keep the contracts department informed of the current contract position regarding progress

(2)   To monitor the key dates relating to the receipt of information at site management level.   This information may later be used to establish the validity of claims where delays to the progress of work have subsequently occurred

(3)   To provide a detailed record of contract resources including labour, plant and material utilisation

(4)   To report problem areas relating to labour, material and plant requirements which are likely to affect future progress

(5)   To report on the progress of subcontractors with particular reference to subcontractors' co-ordination and requirements

(6)   To summarise major instructions received from the architect in the form of verbal or written instructions

5.4.2   Information to be Included in Weekly Reports

Many building firms utilise a standard weekly progress report designed to collect data relative to the firm's individual requirements.   The information contained in the weekly report includes

(1)   Contract Information

Name of project and site manager.   Date and current week number. Contract commencement and completion dates.

(2) Current Progress

A review of the current progress position will be indicated.
The site operations currently being undertaken will be critically
reviewed in sequence indicating the number of days each is ahead
or behind programme.   The percentage completion for each operation may also be stated together with an assessment of the completion date.

(3) Future Progress

A review of the operations to be undertaken in the following week
may be reviewed in order to indicate the action planned to ensure
progress on operations behind schedule.

(4) Labour Summary

This will include all labour employed on the project including
both domestic and nominated subcontractors.   A labour return
will be required to be submitted to the clerk of works for inclusion in his report to the architect.

(5) Subcontractors

A review of subcontractors' progress may be indicated in order to
highlight operational problems, sequences or delays.   Subcontractors' requirements for the immediate short term period may be
reviewed in order that pressure may be brought to bear on them
by both the site and contracts manager.

(6) Plant

This will include a summary of plant currently used on site
together with any urgent requirements for the immediate period.
Plant awaiting return to head office or the hirer should be listed
together with instructions for collection or return.   Here again,
pressure may be brought to bear upon the plant department by the
contracts manager.   This will assist in keeping weekly plant
costs to a minimum.

(7) Information Requirements

Information requirements in the immediate short term period may
be reviewed.   This includes information from the following sources

(a) The Architect

A summary of outstanding information relating to drawings, dimensions, detail and instructions may be summarised.   Key information
relating to nominations and subcontractors' queries may also be
raised.

(b)   The Consulting Engineer

This will include data relating to bending schedules, structural drawings, setting out dimensions and the details of service ducts and openings through floors.

(c)   The Contractor's Head Office

The key information here relates mainly to material and subcontractors' orders.   Shortages of key labour may also be highlighted. Copies of relevant letters must also be circulated to the site manager to keep him informed of matters directly affecting the site and head office liaison with other parties.

(8)   Drawings Received

A summary of all new and revised drawings issued must be indicated. It is often the policy of the company to circulate drawings through the contractor's head office.   These may then be circulated by the office manager to the appropriate personnel, e.g. contracts manager, site, quantity surveyors and buyer.

(9)   Weather Conditions

A summary of the weather conditions over the past week is an essential part of site records.   This enables lost time to be assessed due to inclement weather and may later be used to formulate an application for an extension of time.   A record of lost time will be submitted to the clerk of works for inclusion in his weekly report to the architect.

(10)   Urgent Requirements

The major areas requiring action by the head office may be summarised.   Items appearing in this section will need immediate action by the contracts manager or construction director.

(11)   Other Relevant Information

This may contain details of visitors to site.

Copies of the weekly site report are circulated to the contracts manager and a copy is retained on site.

5.4.3   The Clerk of Works' Report

An awareness of site conditions and progress must be maintained by the architect during the contract.   This will involve the clerk of works submitting weekly progress reports to include the following information

(1)   The main contractor's daily labour force

(2)   Subcontractor's daily labour force

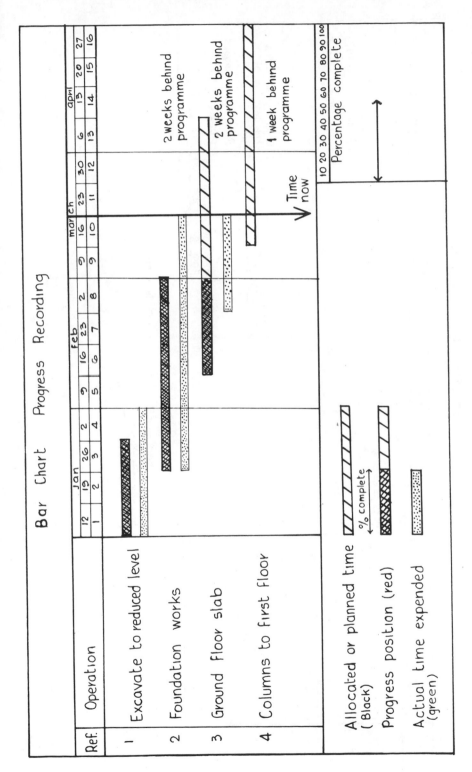

Figure 5.7

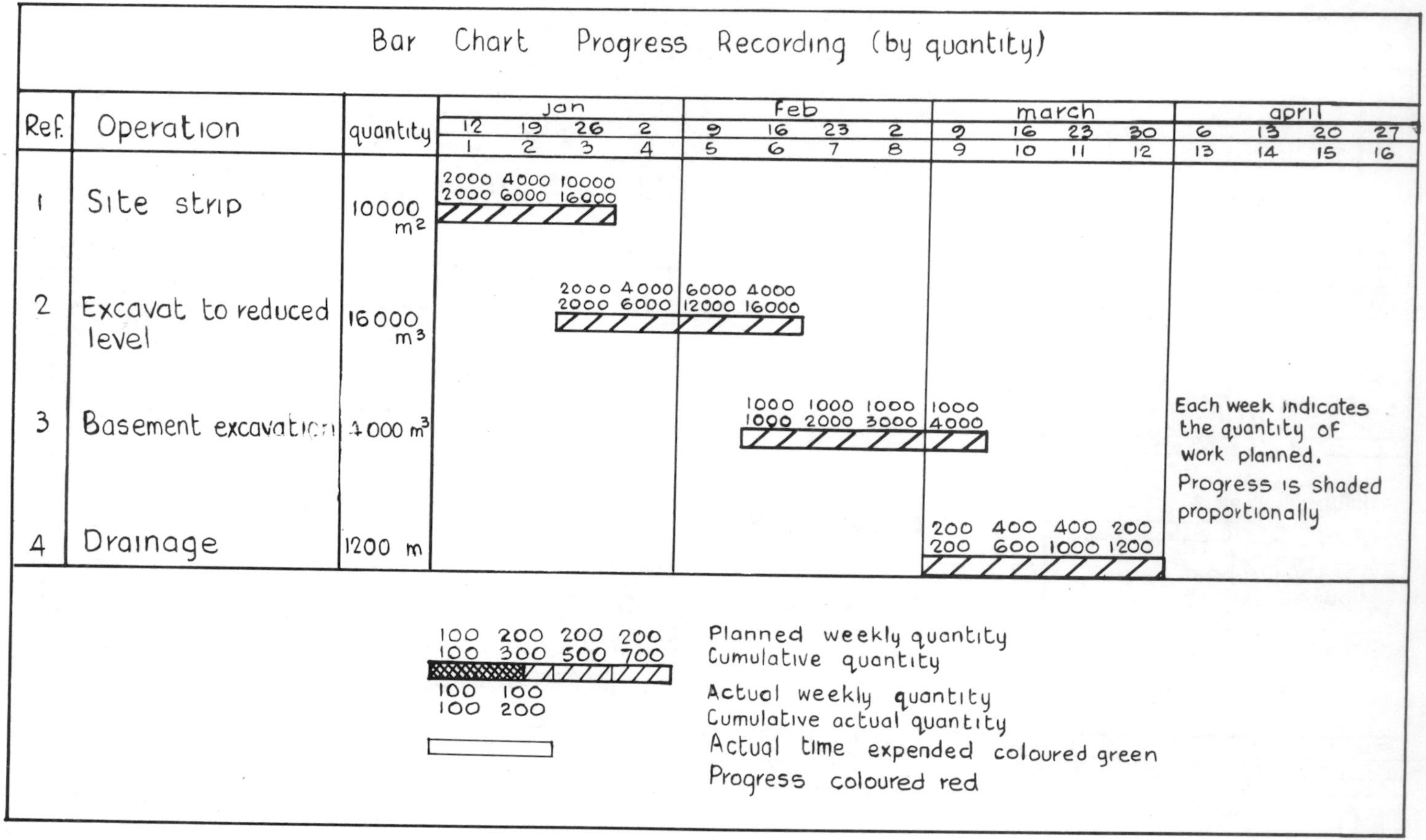

Figure 5.8

Bar Chart Progress Recording (by quantity)

Ref.	Operation	quantity	Jan 12 / 1	19 / 2	26 / 3	2 / 4	Feb 9 / 5	16 / 6	23 / 7	2 / 8	9 / 9	march 16 / 10	23 / 11	30 / 12	6 / 13	april 13 / 14	20 / 15	27 / 16
1	Site strip	10000 m²	2000 2000	4000 6000	10000 10900													
2	Excavat to reduced level	16000 m³			2000 2000	4000 6000	6000 12000	4000 16000										
3	Basement excavation 4000 m³						1000 1000	1000 2000	1000 3000	1000 4000							
4	Drainage	1200 m									200 200	400 600	400 1000	200 1200				

Each week indicates the quantity of work planned. Progress is shaded proportionally

100 200 200 200
100 300 500 700

Planned weekly quantity
Cumulative quantity

100 100
100 200

Actual weekly quantity
Cumulative actual quantity
Actual time expended coloured green
Progress coloured red

(3) Materials delivered to site during the week

(4) An assessment of labour or plant shortages affecting
     progress

(5) Areas of major delays together with an assessment of
     the number of days ahead or behind programme

(6) Daily weather record including time lost per day and
     per week

(7) Drawings issued to the contractor

(8) Instructions to be confirmed by the architect

(9) Brief report on the overall progress relating to
     specific operations

(10) Visitors attending site during the week

The clerk of works' report assists in providing a factual
record of contract events and progress from commencement to
completion of the project.   Such records may prove invaluable
to the architect when considering contractual claims put forward
by the contractor.

5.4.4 Programme Updating

In order to monitor progress accurately the contract programme
must be updated at the end of each week.   The procedure in
recording progress on bar charts is illustrated on Figures 5.7
and 5.8.

A copy of the marked-up programme can be posted to the contractor's head office on the Monday morning of each week.   The progress
position will then be transferred onto the head office programme
and the original returned to site by the following Friday.   In
this way a "shuttle" programme is circulated between the project
and head office each week.

On larger projects the responsibility for progress recording
will be with the site planning engineer or production controller.

5.5 WEEKLY COST CONTROL

The following example outlines the principles of a weekly cost
control system which is directly related to the short-term
planning activities at site level.   The weekly planning is undertaken by a site planning engineer working closely with the site
manager and general foreman.   Alternatively the short-term
planning may be the responsibility of the site engineer on a
civil engineering contract.   At the weekly planning meeting the
plan of work for the following week will be prepared and agreed
and this will form the basis of the cost control system.

229

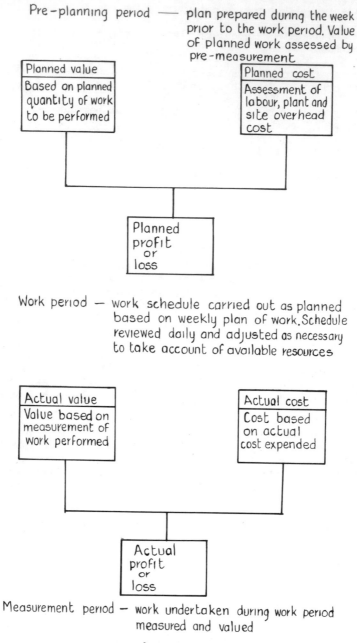

Pre-planning period — plan prepared during the week prior to the work period. Value of planned work assessed by pre-measurement

Planned value
Based on planned quantity of work to be performed

Planned cost
Assessment of labour, plant and site overhead cost

Planned profit or loss

Work period — work schedule carried out as planned based on weekly plan of work. Schedule reviewed daily and adjusted as necessary to take account of available resources

Actual value
Value based on measurement of work performed

Actual cost
Cost based on actual cost expended

Actual profit or loss

Measurement period — work undertaken during work period measured and valued

figure 5.9

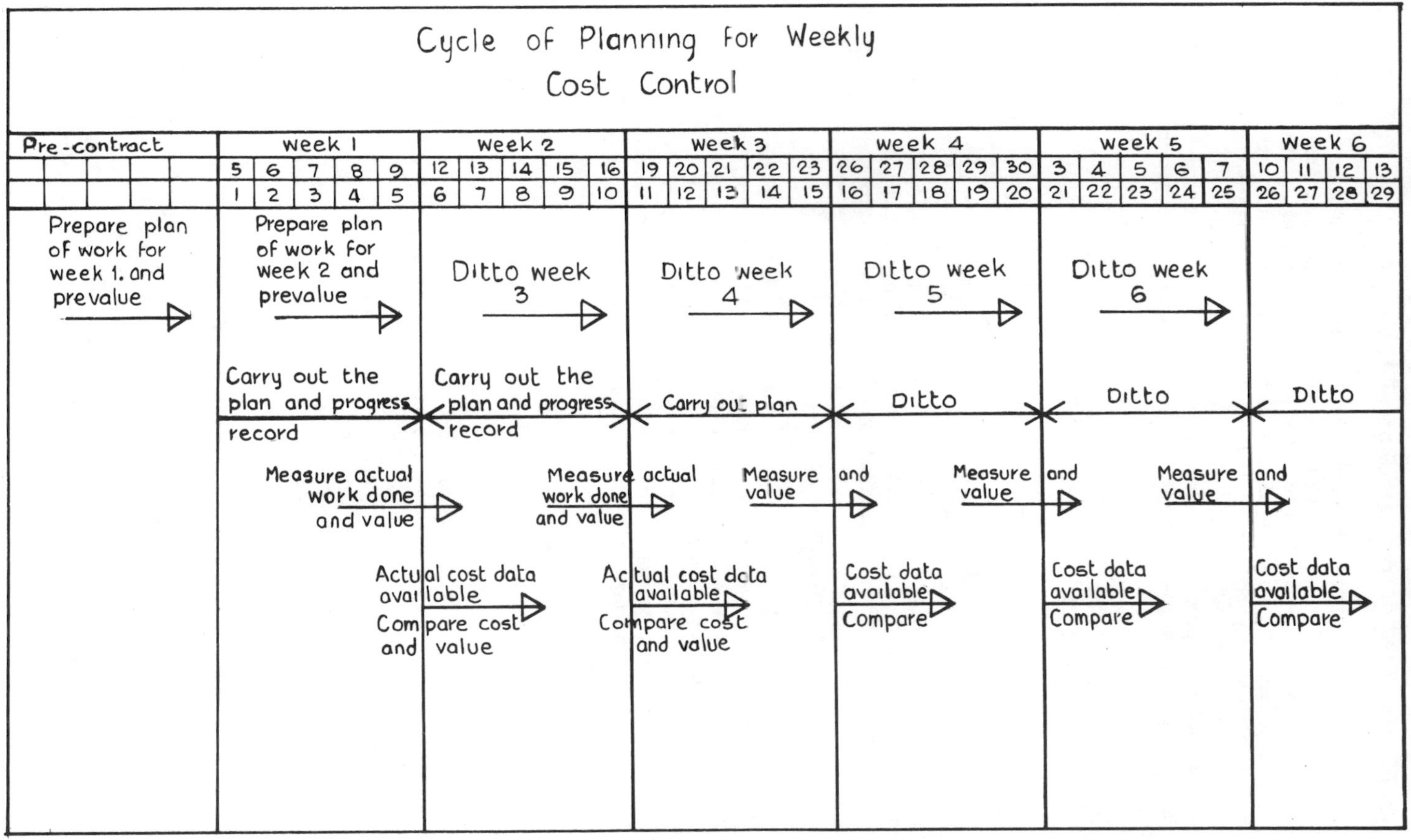

Cycle of Planning for Weekly Cost Control

Pre-contract	Week 1			Week 2			Week 3			Week 4			Week 5			Week 6		
	5	6	7	8	9	12	13	14	15	16	19	20	21	22	23	26	27	28	29	30	3	4	5	6	7	10	11	12	13
	1	2	3	4	5	6	7	8	9	10	11	12	13	14	15	16	17	18	19	20	21	22	23	24	25	26	27	28	29

Prepare plan of work for week 1, and prevalue

Prepare plan of work for week 2 and prevalue

Ditto week 3

Ditto week 4

Ditto week 5

Ditto week 6

Carry out the plan and progress record

Carry out the plan and progress record

Carry out plan

Ditto

Ditto

Ditto

Measure actual work done and value

Measure actual work done and value

Measure actual work done and value

Measure and value

Measure and value

Measure and value

Actual cost data available

Compare cost and value

Actual cost data available

Compare cost and value

Actual cost data available

Compare cost and value

Cost data available

Compare

Cost data available

Compare

Cost data available

Compare

Figure 5.10

5.5.1 Principles of the Cost Control System

The cost control procedures involve the pre-measurement of work in the short term. This involves pre-measuring and pre-valuing the work to be undertaken during the following week. The cost of undertaking the work is also assessed in order that the planned profit or loss may be determined. Figure 5.9 outlines the principles of the cost control system during the pre-planning period, working period and measurement period. Figure 5.10 illustrates the sequence to a time scale during the progress of work.

5.5.2 Operation of the Cost and Planning System – Assessment of the Planned Value and Planned Cost

The weekly site plan of work is prepared on the Friday of each week. The format of presentation is illustrated in Figure 5.11. This involves indicating the work to be undertaken during the next weekly period for each trade gang. The work content of the plan must be a realistic assessment of the work taking into account the opinion of the site foreman and requirements of the monthly plan of work. Descriptions used on the plan must be sufficiently detailed to enable the quantity of the work to be assessed from the drawings.

Figures 5.12 and 5.13 indicate the weekly cost statement. The quantity of work abstracted from the weekly plan of work is pre-measured from the drawings, entered on the form and pre-valued by applying the net bill rates for labour and plant. This enables the planned value of work to be assessed. From the previous week's labour and plant costs an assessment may be prepared of the planned cost for undertaking the work during the next weekly period.

By comparing the planned value with the planned cost the planned profit or loss may be assessed.

The weekly cost statement in Figure 5.13 indicates a planned value in the sum of £3823 compared with a planned cost of £3572, the resulting planned gain amounts to £251 for the week.

As net labour and plant rates are being used for building up the weekly cost assessment, any resulting forecast gain is additional profit over that which is anticipated. A satisfactory position may be assumed therefore where the planned cost and value equate.

5.5.3 Assessment of the Actual Value and Actual Cost

During the carrying out of the weekly site plan of work, progress is recorded daily and the work ahead kept under constant review. On the Monday following, the actual work completed the previous week is measured and entered on the cost statement. This is valued at the target rates and the actual value of the work completed assessed.

232

Contract Hillgate

Weekly Plan of Work

Date 8 June 1981

From 8 June to 15 June week no. 12.

Labour gang	Gang size	Plant	Monday	Tuesday	Wednesday	Thursday	Friday	Remarks
Bricklayers gang 1	4 bl. 2 lab.	mixer	Basement wall line a to d overall height 3 m.	Basement wall line a to d overall height 3 m.	External wall a to d 1 lift	Front boundary wall lift 1.5 m high	Front boundary wall lift 1.5 m high	
Carpenters gang 1	2 carp. 1 lab.		Formwork to beams line d, e, f	Formwork to suspended d, e, f	Formwork to columns 1-4	Strike beams line d, e, f	Fwk to beams line g, h	
Labour gang 1	4 lab.	J.C.B. 4 dumper vibrator	Temporary hardstanding to churchgate	Temporary hardstanding to churchgate	Concrete beams d, e, f	Concrete columns 1-4	Excavate pad Fdt to canopy	
		J.C.B. 4			Drainage Reddish	connection Road		
	13 no.							

Figure 5.11

233

Weekly Cost Statement

Contract   Week No.

W/E

Bill ref.	Description of work	Target Labour and plant	Plan Measured quantity	Plan Value	Actual Measured quantity	Actual Value	Cost assessment Build-up	Cost assessment Planned	Cost assessment Actual

Total labour and plant value   Actual value

Deduct total cost   Actual cost

Gain or loss   Gain or loss

Figure 5.12

Contract Hillgate Weekly Cost Statement Week no. 8

W/E 16 november 1981 Sheet 1

Bill ref.	Description of work	Target Labour and plant	Plan Measured quantity	Plan Value	Actual Measured quantity	Actual Value	Cost assessment Build up	Planned	Actual
48b	One brick wall in basement	£3·00	200 m²	600	205	615	Labour	1300	1285
489	328 wall in basement	5·50	200 m²	1100	214	1177	+110% on cost	1430	1413
68b	215 wall in boundary	4·50	300 m²	1350	250	1125	Plant		
38f	Fix formwork to beams	1·50	200 m²	300	170	255	Mixers 2no	60	48
39b	Fix formwork to columns	2·00	40 m²	80	35	70	hoist	80	68
24b	Temporary crossing	£172	item	172	item	107	J.C.B. 4	360	326
							dumper	78	58
34a	Excavate pad foundations	1·00	30 m³	30	45	45	vibrator	36	26
36b	Concrete beams	5·50	20 m³	110	18	99			
36g	Concrete columns	6·50	6 m³	39	4	26	Administration	180	140
34f	Remove excavated material	1·40	30	42	45	63	Supervision	48	68
							Accomodation		
	Total labour and plant value			3823	Actual value	3582			3572
	Deduct total cost			3572	Actual cost	3432			3432
			Planned gain	251	Actual gain	150			

Figure 5.13

235

On the Wednesday of the week the data relating to the actual costs incurred will be available for entry onto the cost statement. This will include the total labour cost from the wage sheets and the plant charges from the plant returns. The total actual cost may now be compared with the actual value and the actual gain or loss assessed.

The validity of the short-term planning may now be realistically assessed by comparing the planned situation with the actual cost position.

The data set out in Figure 5.13 indicates a planned gain of £251 and an actual gain of £150. This has resulted from the non-completion of the temporary crossing and an over-assessment of brickwork to the boundary wall. There has also been a corresponding reduction in the labour and plant costs.

5.5.4 The Effectiveness of the Cost System

The principles of the cost system outlined have proved effective in application in medium and large sized contracting organisations. The system may be applied to individual gangs on a large project and it works particularly well on civil engineering projects where a smaller number of operations are involved. The cost system may be ably controlled by a site engineer, planner or production controller. It is of importance to the success of the system that site management fully understand the system and keenly participate in the short-term planning activities. Team work is essential between trades foremen, subcontractors, general foremen, planning engineer and site manager.

5.6 MATERIALS CONTROL AND ITS RELATIONSHIP TO SHORT-TERM PLANNING

The objectives of an early warning system of materials control related to monthly and weekly planning at site management level is to be outlined. The example is to be related to the construction of a factory project and is to illustrate the integration of material requirements into the programming sequence.

5.6.1 Objectives of a Materials Control System

(1) To assess material requirements so as to allow for periods of manufacture, distribution and delivery appropriate to the construction situation.

(2) To facilitate forward planning thus enabling material supplies and prices to be fully evaluated

(3) To enable checks to be made on material utilisation with the objective of controlling or reducing wastage

(4) To enable key materials which affect the construction progress to be incorporated into the contract programme.

Material Schedule Summary						
Contract						
Date				Sheet No.		
Ref.	Material	Bill ref.	Supplier	Order number	Date ordered	Date required

Figure 5.14

Subcontractors Summary							
Contract							
Date					Sheet No.		
Ref.	Subcontractor	Trade	Order number	Date order placed	Date required on site	Date notified	Bill ref.

Figure 5.15

(5)   To take advantage of favourable trading conditions, and, where applicable, bulk buying facilities

(6)   To enable site management to assess the influence of materials on planning procedures and site layout

(7)   To incorporate material requirements into the planning process

(8)   To keep management aware of the control aspects arising from aspects of materials demand and supply

5.6.2   Head Office Responsibility for Materials Control

Company policy must clearly indicate responsibility for materials control and purchasing procedures.   Centralised purchasing is the usual policy within the larger construction firms.   The buying department may be responsible for placing material orders and all subcontractors' orders.   Alternatively the buying department may place orders for materials only and subcontractors' contracts drawn up by the quantity surveying department.

Material quantities prior to ordering should be checked from the contract drawings.   Where this is not possible, provisional orders may be placed based on the quantities indicated in the bills of quantities, and later confirmed prior to delivery.

Material scheduling can be considered part of the buying function or be related to the long and short-term planning procedures.   A production or materials controller may be responsible for co-ordinating material requirements to suit its site programme in the short-term.   In this way the responsibility for calling forward key materials is removed from the site manager and becomes part of the planning function.

An example of a materials schedule is indicated in Figure 5.14 and a summary of subcontractors' requirements information is shown in Figure 5.15.   These may be placed at the front of the material schedules, take-off sheets or subcontractors' quotations and orders.   They form a summary to the documentation and contain key dates of importance to the site manager.

5.6.3   A Materials Early Warning System

For the construction of a factory project the key material and subcontractors' requirements may be integrated into the planning procedures.   This involves the utilisation of material control symbols directly on the material schedule or programme.   The symbols used are indicated in Figure 5.16.   The symbols may be entered on the master programme to indicate key dates in relation to individual operations.   This, however, does not aid updating. A separate materials schedule which contains key dates and enables continuous updating is illustrated in the form of an early warning system.   The procedure in setting up the early warning system is as follows

Material Control Symbols

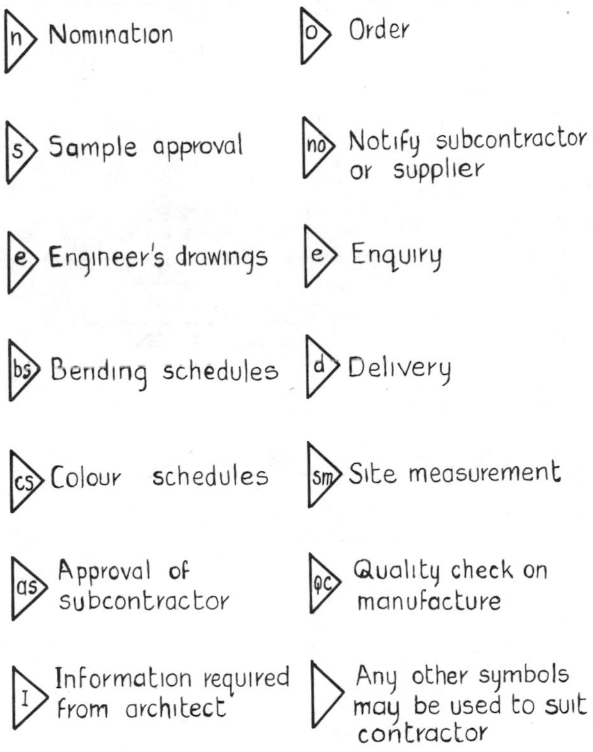

⊳n Nomination   ⊳o Order

⊳s Sample approval   ⊳no Notify subcontractor
                          or supplier

⊳e Engineer's drawings ⊳e Enquiry

⊳bs Bending schedules   ⊳d Delivery

⊳cs Colour schedules   ⊳sm Site measurement

⊳as Approval of   ⊳qc Quality check on
    subcontractor   manufacture

⊳I Information required ⊳ Any other symbols
   from architect   may be used to suit
                            contractor

figure 5.16

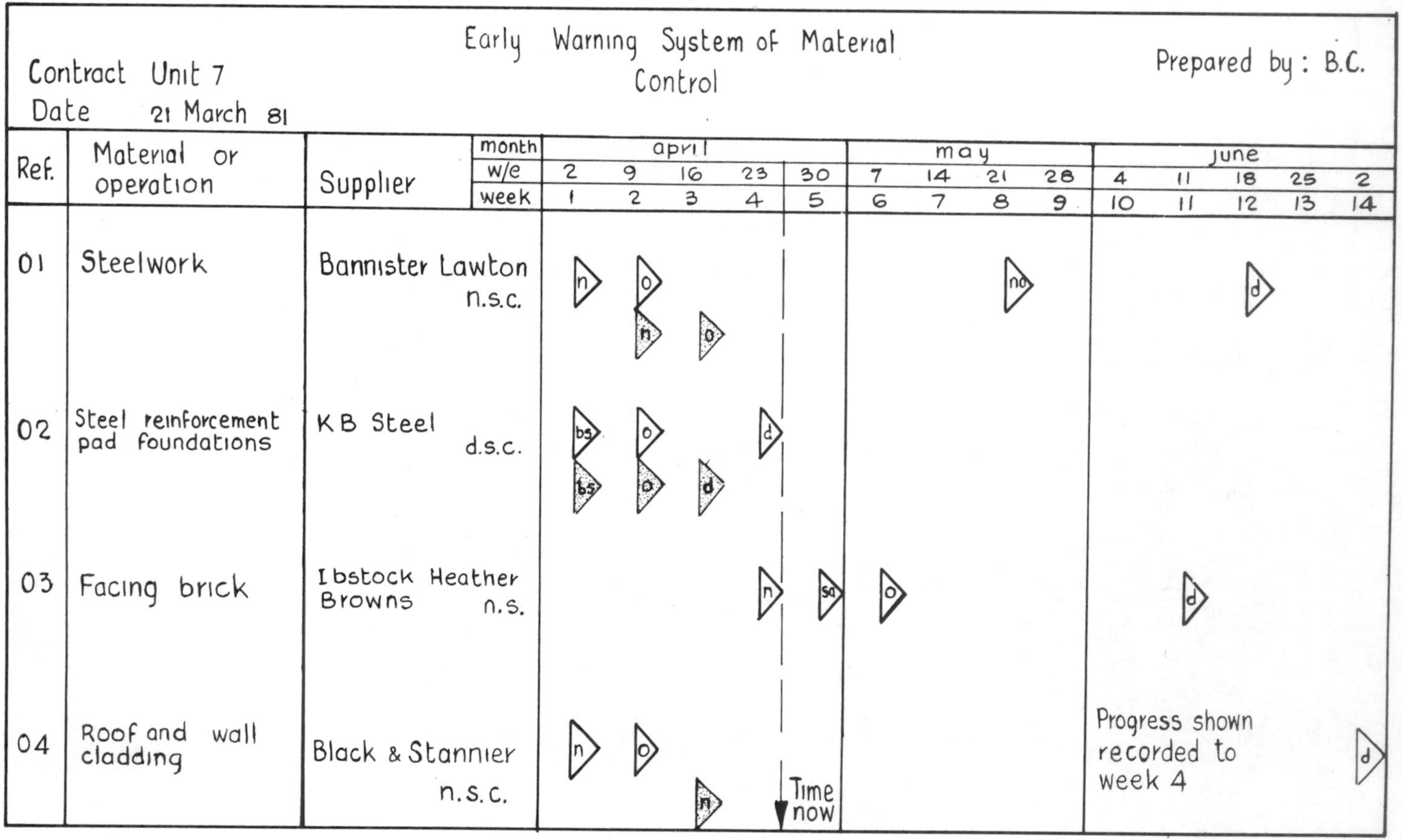

Contract Unit 7
Date 21 March 81
Early Warning System of Material Control
Prepared by: B.C.
Ref.
Material or operation
Supplier
month
w/e
week
april
may
june
2 9 16 23 30 7 14 21 28 4 11 18 25 2
1 2 3 4 5 6 7 8 9 10 11 12 13 14
01
Steelwork
Bannister Lawton n.s.c.
02
Steel reinforcement pad foundations
K B Steel d.s.c.
03
Facing brick
Ibstock Heather Browns n.s.
04
Roof and wall cladding
Black & Stannier n.s.c.
Time now
Progress shown recorded to week 4

figure 5.17

(1) Prepare a schedule of operations relating to the programme and key material requirements relating to them

(2) Insert symbols to indicate the planned course of information to be made available

(3) As the contract progresses indicate new symbols on the lower line of each item in order to show when the task has been carried out

(4) Colour the actual symbol in red when the task has been completed or the information received

(5) Update as required as work progresses and take corrective action to ensure that the plan is maintained

The early warning system pictorially shows the relationship between material requirements and site operations highlighting the effect of delays in the release of information or material deliveries on the progress of work.

Figure 5.17 illustrates an extract from an early warning materials schedule marked up to show the progress position during a factory project. The materials control schedule is prepared in the pre-contract planning period and may be extended during the contract planning stage as further information is made available to the contractor. Throughout the contract period the schedule must be updated to show the relationship between the planned and actual dates relating to the release of information.

Data of this type relating to the release of information can be utilised in the preparation of claims, especially where the item can be directly related to a delay in progress.

5.6.4 The Utilisation of Symbols on the Contract Programme

An extract from the master programme is illustrated in Figure 5.18 to show the relationship between programmed operations and information of material requirements. The symbol may be shaded in red to show when the information has been made available and a record of the date of the appropriate release recorded alongside.

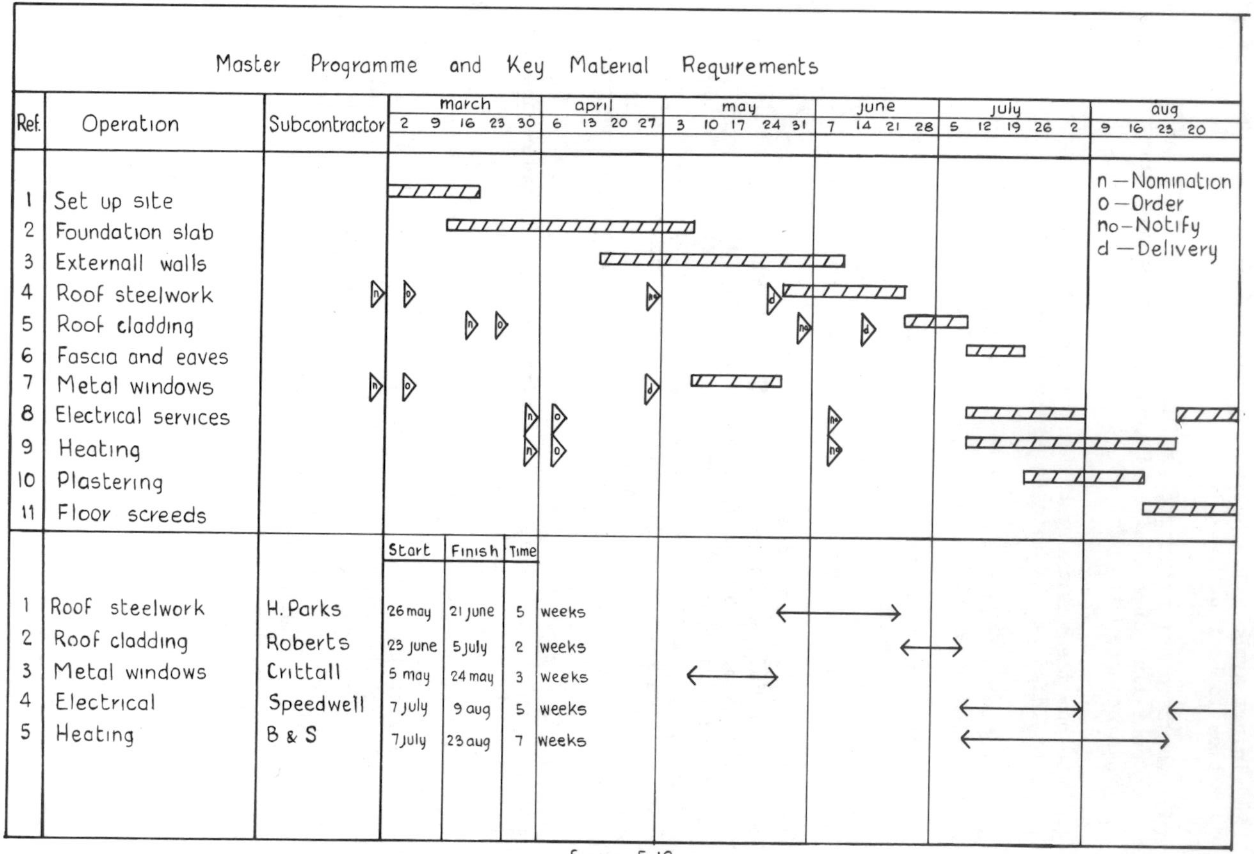

Master Programme and Key Material Requirements
Ref.
Operation
Subcontractor
march
2 9 16 23 30
april
6 13 20 27
may
3 10 17 24 31
june
7 14 21 28
july
5 12 19 26 2
aug
9 16 23 20
1 Set up site
2 Foundation slab
3 Externall walls
4 Roof steelwork
5 Roof cladding
6 Fascia and eaves
7 Metal windows
8 Electrical services
9 Heating
10 Plastering
11 Floor screeds
n — Nomination
o — Order
no — Notify
d — Delivery
Start
Finish
Time
1 Roof steelwork
H. Parks
26 may
21 june
5 weeks
2 Roof cladding
Roberts
23 june
5 july
2 weeks
3 Metal windows
Crittall
5 may
24 may
3 weeks
4 Electrical
Speedwell
7 july
9 aug
5 weeks
5 Heating
B & S
7 july
23 aug
7 weeks

Figure 5.18

6 FUNDING FOR SPECULATIVE CONTRACTS

6.1 CASH FUNDING AND THE SPECULATIVE DEVELOPER

Introduction

Cash funding requirements for the speculative developer/contractor
differ considerably from those of the contractor being paid on
interim certificates.   Speculative developments involve a high
degree of risk and a good understanding of the market - whether it
be speculative housing or an office/factory development project.

One needs and understanding bank manager when market trends
change during a dveleopment project.   The developer must first
produce a realistic feasibility study, which should take into account all possible cost factors and be based on a realistic time
schedule.

'Time' - to a developer, is 'money'.   If the profit release
forecast is based on completing the project within say a 10-month
period, then this time scale must be met.   Assessment of the time
scale should allow for contingencies, such as the pre-contract
planning procedures, obtaining building regulations and a realistic construction period.   Interest on locked-up capital can easily
erode profits; if the market conditions change during the project
then delayed sales may eat further into the all-too-slim margins.

    Residual Value = Difference between the forecast expenditure
                     and
                     The forecast income from sales.

    Residual Value = Income from sales - forecast expenditure.

The residual value may in effect be the project profit release.
This may be expressed as a total monetary sum or as a percentage
of the income from sales.

If the residual value is a minus figure, then the project is
not feasible.

6.2 ASSESSMENT OF PROJECT FEASIBILITY

On a housing development, the forecast expenditure may be built up
from consideration of the following:

Forecast expenditure (MONEY OUT)

Cost of land - site purchase cost
             - interest on capital for site purchase

Development fees
             - Planning/building regulation fees
             - Architectural/surveying fees
             - Design consultant
             - Legal fees for land purchase
             - Sales fees
             - Legal conveyancing fees

Site works
             - Site clearance/demolition works
             - Roads and footpaths
             - Foul and surface water sewers
             - Services to site
             - Entrance works (if applicable)

Building cost
             - Cost assessment of building elements
             - Interest charges on siteworks and
                building cost
             - Landscape works

Income from sales (MONEY IN)

   Income from sales is dependent upon house type, quality
   of building and the tone of the development area.

   Selling price requires careful assessment of market
   conditions.

   The developer at this stage may decide to consult a
   crystal ball.

Residual Value = Income from Sales - Forecast Expenditure
     PROFIT   MONEY IN   MONEY OUT

The calculation of the interest is dependent upon the time relationship. The shorter the overall project period, the less the
interest charges will be. Consideration is necessary for the
interest calculation on the land, siteworks and building cost.
Figure 6.1 illustrates the time/expenditure relationship relative
to the major stages of the work.

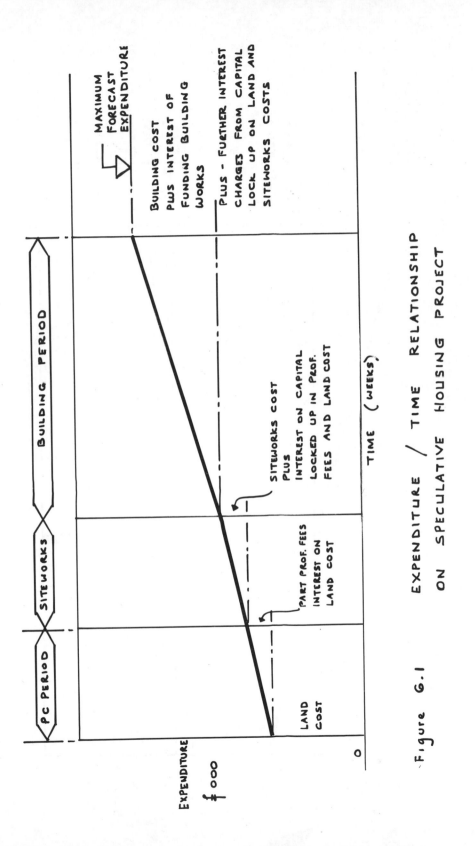

Figure 6.1 EXPENDITURE / TIME RELATIONSHIP
ON SPECULATIVE HOUSING PROJECT

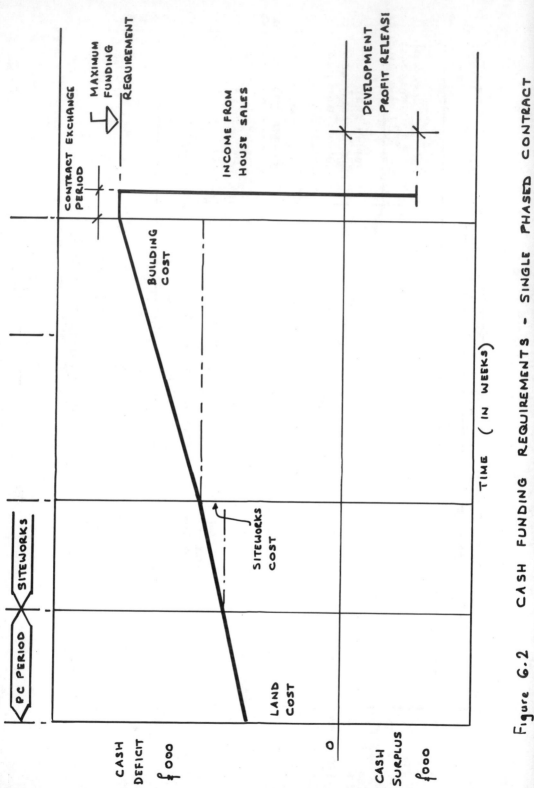

Figure 6.2   CASH FUNDING REQUIREMENTS - SINGLE PHASED CONTRACT

6.3   PATTERN OF CASH FUNDING REQUIREMENTS FOR A SPECULATIVE
      DEVELOPMENT

The illustration is based on the development of a speculative housing contract for the construction of two house units.

   Based on the assumption that both houses would be constructed
simultaneously and be sold on completion of building, the cash
funding requirements would be similar to those shown in Figure 6.2.

   In order to improve the cash funding requirements (and subsequently reduce the maximum cash required) consideration may be given
to the following:

1.   Initial deposits are to be taken from the purchasers of the
     two house units.   This is based on the assumption that pur-
     chasers have been found prior to the commencement of building
     works on site.

     The initial deposit of say 10% will have a marked effect on the
     cash funding position.

2.   Construct Unit 1 first, i.e. build in two distinct phases.
     Use the profit release from Unit 1 to assist in funding the
     construction of Unit 2.

     This will have a more dramatic effect on the cash funding
     requirements for the project and reduce the client's funding
     considerably.

     Many housing projects developed by National contractors are
     undertaken in phases as an aid to the cash funding situation.

     Figure 6.3 illustrates the effect of implementary phasing and
     the introduction of initial deposits on the funding position.

3.   The developer may consider imposing a series of stage payments
     on the house purchaser.   Monies may be released at specified
     stages of construction, i.e.

                    10% - initial deposit on commencement
                    20% - completion of ground floor slab
                    30% - completion of roof
                    30% completion of final fixings
                    10% - on handover

   Stage payment procedures may be applied on small developments
undertaken by local developers.   Administrative procedures may
however make the process of stage payments rather cumbersome for
the larger developer.

   The funding pattern based on a stage payment system is shown
in Figure 6.4.

247

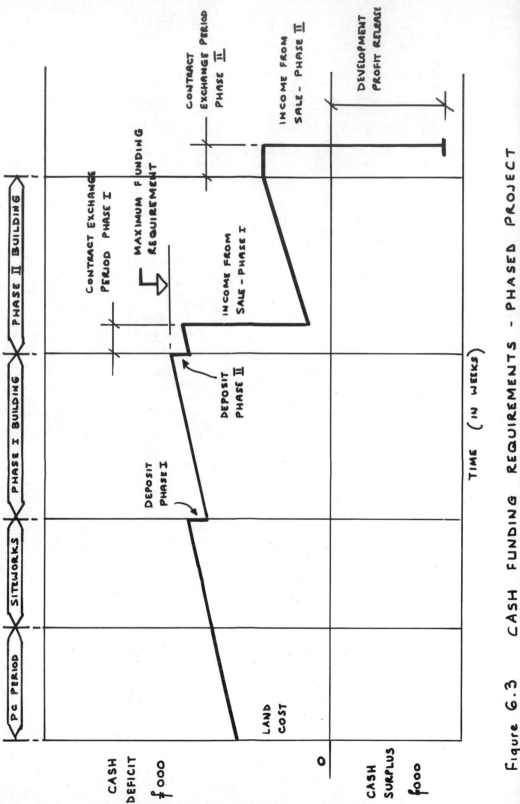

Figure 6.3   CASH FUNDING REQUIREMENTS - PHASED PROJECT

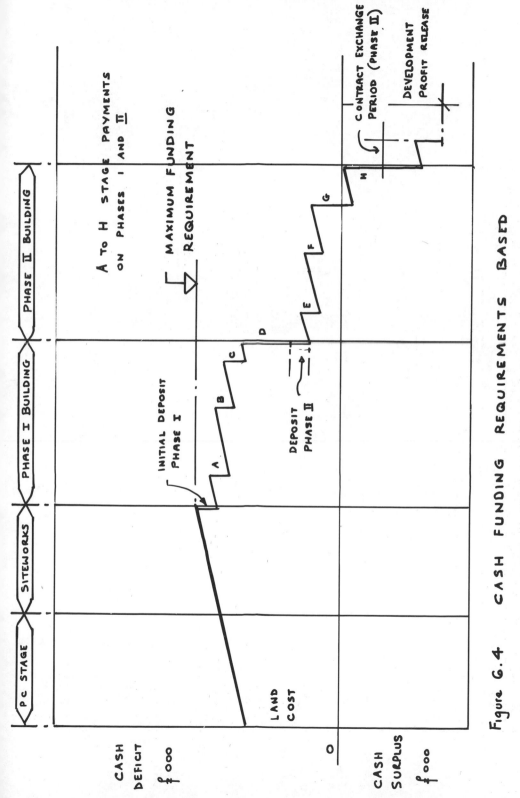

Figure 6.4   CASH FUNDING REQUIREMENTS BASED
ON   STAGE   PAYMENTS